COMITE EURO-INTERNATIONAL DU BETON

# DESIGN OF FASTENINGS IN CONCRETE

DESIGN GUIDE

Thomas Telford

Published by Thomas Telford Publishing, Thomas Telford Services Ltd, 1 Heron Quay, London E14 4JD, UK for the Comité Euro-International du Béton, Case Postale 88, CH-1015 Lausanne, Switzerland

First published 1995 as CEB Bulletin d'Information No. 226 'Design of fastenings in concrete'.
Thomas Telford edition published 1997

Distributors for Thomas Telford books are
*USA:* American Society of Civil Engineers, Publications Sales Department, 345 East 47th Street, New York, NY 10017-2398
*Japan:* Maruzen Co. Ltd, Book Department, 3–10 Nihonbashi 2-chome, Chuo-ku, Tokyo 103
*Australia:* DA Books and Journals, 648 Whitehorse Road, Mitcham 3132, Victoria

A catalogue record for this book is available from the British Library

**Classification**
*Availability:* Unrestricted
*Contents:* Guidance based on research and best current practice
*Status:* Committee guided
*Users:* Civil and structural engineers, designers

ISBN: 0 7277 2558 0

Typeset by MHL Typesetting Ltd, Coventry
Printed in Great Britain by Redwood Books, Trowbridge, Wilts

# Preface

Modern fastening technique is increasingly employed for the transfer of concentrated loads into concrete and masonry structures. Cast-in-place systems (which are placed in the formwork before casting of the concrete) and post-installed systems (which are installed in hardened structural concrete or masonry) are equally common.

The load is transferred into the base material by mechanical interlock, friction, bond or a combination of these mechanisms. In general independent of the load-transfer mechanism, fastenings rely on the tensile capacity of concrete or masonry.

Although a large number of fastening assemblies are installed every day, understanding in the engineering community about their behaviour is generally very limited. Furthermore, there is no generally accepted design method.

In order to improve the general knowledge and awareness of the engineering profession in this area, Task Group III/5: *Fastenings to reinforced concrete and masonry structures* was formed by the CEB in 1987.

The group produced a state-of-the-art report on fastenings to concrete and masonry structures, first published as Bulletins 206 and 207 in 1991 by the CEB and in a revised version as a book by Thomas Telford in 1994. Since then the Task Group has concentrated on two topics:

(1) a guide for the design of fastenings in concrete;
(2) a state-of-the-art report on the design and application of fastenings for seismic retrofitting.

Meetings have been held in the following locations:

Abisko (June 1992)
San Juan (October 1992)
Santorini (May 1993)
Prague (November 1993)
San Francisco (March 1994)
Arles (September 1994)
Kyoto (May 1995)

In this book a guide for the design of fastenings in concrete is proposed. It was presented to, and approved by, the 30th CEB Plenary Session in Berlin in September 1995.

The design guide is based on the safety concept of partial safety factors and covers all loading directions and failure modes. It takes into account the current state of the art and is valid for expansion, undercut and headed anchors. It is applicable to both new construction and the repair and strengthening of existing structures. In the future, the guide will be extended to cover fastenings with bonded anchors, channel bars and shear lugs as well as applications subjected to seismic excitations.

Rolf Eligehausen
*Convenor of the Task Group*
Stuttgart, October 1996

# Acknowledgements

This CEB Guide for the design of fastenings in concrete has been written by the CEB Task Group III/5: *Fastenings to reinforced concrete and masonry structures.*

| | | |
|---|---|---|
| Convenor: | Rolf, Eligehausen | Germany |
| Technical Secretary: | Konrad Bergmeister | Austria |
| Members: | Didier Bourette | |
| | (since October 1994) | France |
| | Marc Combette | |
| | (until October 1994) | France |
| | Ronald A. Cook | USA |
| | Vicky A. Covert | USA |
| | Lennart Elfgren | Sweden |
| | Paul Hollenbach | USA |
| | Dick Hordijk | The Netherlands |
| | James O. Jirsa | USA |
| | Ben Kato | Japan |
| | Richard E. Klingner | USA |
| | Christoph Körner | Germany |
| | Harry B. Lancelot | USA |
| | Klaus Laternser | Germany |
| | Yasuhiro Matsuzaki | Japan |
| | Lee Mattis | |
| | (since August 1994) | USA |
| | Bruno Mesureur | France |
| | Yoshiaki Nakano | Japan |
| | Tsuneo Okada | Japan |
| | Walker S. Paterson | |
| | (until February 1993) | United Kingdom |
| | Peter Pusill-Wachtsmuth | Germany |
| | Manfred Rinklake | |
| | (until April 1994) | Germany |
| | Hans-Dieter Seghezzi | |
| | (until September 1992) | Liechtenstein |
| | John F. Silva | Liechtenstein |
| | Gunnar Söderlind | Sweden |
| | Reiji Tanaka | Japan |
| | Rüdiger Tewes | Switzerland |
| | Johann Tschositsch | Germany |
| | Shigeru Usami | Japan |
| | Elizabeth Vintzeleou | Greece |
| | Harry Wiewel | USA |
| | Richard E. Wollmershauser | USA |
| Invited Guests | Tomoaki Akiyama | Japan |
| | Youji Hosokawa | Japan |
| | Hiroshi Kimura | Japan |
| | Masahide Ohmori | Japan |
| | Masmichi Ohkubo | Japan |
| | Toshi Sekiguchi | Japan |

The final draft of the guide for the design of fastenings has been produced in Stuttgart by an Editorial Board, namely:

| | | |
|---|---|---|
| Convenor: | Rolf Eligehausen | Germany |
| Members: | Ronald A. Cook | USA |
| | Peter Pusill-Wachtsmuth | Germany |
| | John F. Silva | Liechtenstein |
| | Richard E. Wollmershauser | USA |

# Contents

# Introduction

Fastenings are commonly used to transfer loads into concrete structures or to connect concrete elements to each other.

As illustrated in Fig. 1, every connection to concrete is composed of the following basic components:

- the attachment, which is the component connected to the concrete. This is usually of structural steel, and includes a fixture (baseplate). However, it may be made of wood, structural concrete or other materials.
- the anchors themselves, which attach the fixture to the concrete.
- the embedment, consisting of the concrete surrounding each anchor. This is normally described in terms of an embedment depth.

A method is proposed in this Guide to design fastenings in cracked and non-cracked concrete, which is based on the safety concept of the CEB–FIP Model Code 1990 (MC90)[1] and takes into account the current knowledge.[2,3] The component to be anchored may be supported either statically determinate (one or two points of anchorage) or statically indeterminate (more than two points of anchorage) (see Fig. 2). A point of anchorage may consist of one anchor or an anchor group.

In this Guide, only the load transfer into the concrete is covered. The design of the fixture must be performed according to the appropriate code of practice, e.g. in a case of steel fixtures a steel construction code is used.

The Design Guide is valid only if the following conditions are met:

- fastenings are designed by qualified and experienced personnel;
- installation is carried out by personnel having the required skill and experience;
- the structure and (where possible) the anchorage are adequately maintained during their intended life;
- the specified use of the fastening will not be changed for the worse during its intended life unless recalculation is carried out.

*Fig. 1. Basic anchorage nomenclature*

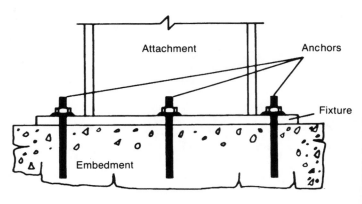

*Fig. 2. Examples of anchored components: (a) statically determinate; (b) statically indeterminate*

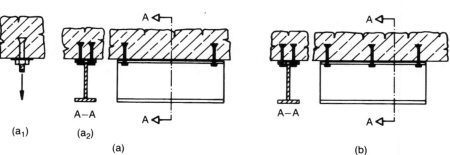

1

*Fig. 3. Flowchart A for the design of fastenings (cross-references given for expansion and undercut anchors)*

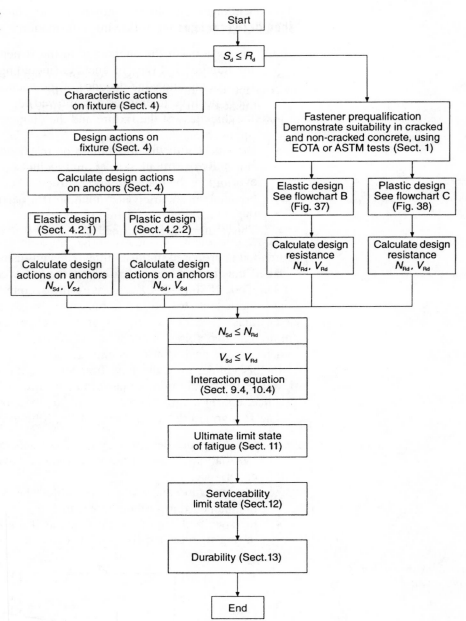

The anchorages should be shown in the construction drawings, which should give at least the following information:

- the location of the anchorage in the structure, including tolerances;
- the number and type of anchors (including the embedment depth);
- the spacing and edge distance of the anchors, including the tolerance (only positive tolerances are allowed);
- the thickness of the fixture and the diameter of the clearance hole (if applicable);
- the position of the attachment on the fixture, including tolerances;
- the maximum thickness of an eventual non-bearing layer below the fixture;
- (special) installation instructions (if applicable).

In addition to the Design Guide a commentary will be prepared as a separate document, which gives the rationale of the proposed provisions. Furthermore, some design examples will be given in the commentary for the convenience of the user.

The Design Guide is subdivided into several parts:

Part I:     General provisions
Part II:    Characteristic resistance of fastenings with post-installed expansion and undercut anchors
Part III:   Characteristic resistance of fastenings with cast-in-place headed anchors
Part IV:    Characteristic resistance of fastenings with bonded anchors
Part V:     Characteristic resistance of fastenings with channel bars
Part VI:    Characteristic resistance of fastenings with shear lugs
Part VII:   Characteristic resistance of fastenings with other anchor types

While Part I gives rules which are valid for all types of anchors, Parts II–VII give provisions which are valid only for a certain type of anchor. Parts IV–VII are in preparation. A flowchart for the design of fastenings with expansion and undercut anchors is given in Fig. 3. Flowcharts for calculating the resistance of fastenings with each type of anchor are given in the part corresponding to that anchor type.

# 1. Scope

## 1.1. Type of anchors, anchor groups

Part I of this Design Guide applies to post-installed expansion (Figs 4 and 5), undercut (Fig. 6) and bonded anchors (Fig. 7) as well as cast-in-place headed anchors (Fig. 8), channel bars (Fig. 9) and shear lugs (Fig. 10). For each expansion anchor type, an example (the upper diagram) along with the anchor installation and splitting forces (shown schematically in the lower diagram) are depicted in Figs 4 and 5. For each undercut anchor type, the drilled hole (left diagram) and the installed anchor (right diagram) are shown in Fig. 6.

The installation, load-transfer mechanisms and behaviour in cracked and non-cracked concrete of the different types of anchors are described in detail in Ref. 3.

Anchors should be suitable for the intended application. The suitability conditions for each anchor type are given in the corresponding Part of this Guide.

*Fig. 4. Typical torque-controlled expansion anchors: (a) single-cone type; (b) double-cone type; (c) taper-bolt type; (d) wedge type; (e) bolt with internally threaded cone*

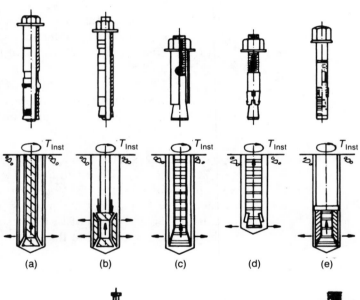

(a)    (b)    (c)    (d)    (e)

*Fig. 5. Typical deformation-controlled expansion anchors: (a) cone-down type ('drop-in anchor'); (b) shank-down type ('drive pin anchor'); (c) cone type; (d) cone type ('self-drill anchor'); (e) plug bolt type*

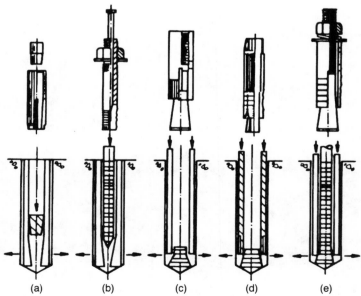

(a)    (b)    (c)    (d)    (e)

*Fig. 6. Typical undercut anchors: undercut is formed before (a)–(c) or during (d), (e) anchor installation*

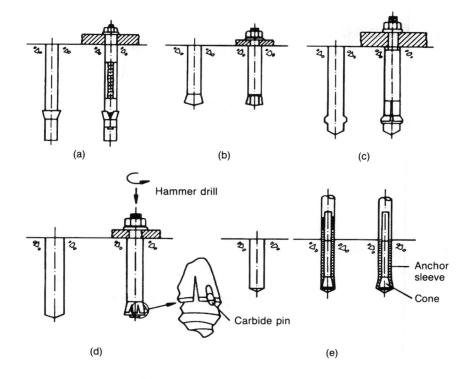

*Fig. 7. Typical bonded anchor*

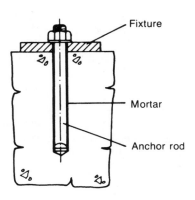

*Fig. 8. Typical headed anchors*

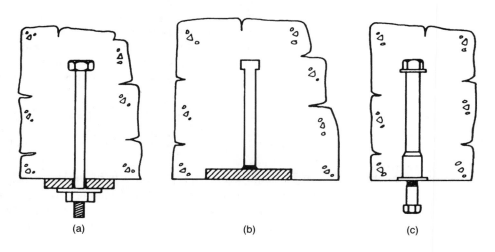

*Fig. 9. Typical channel bar*

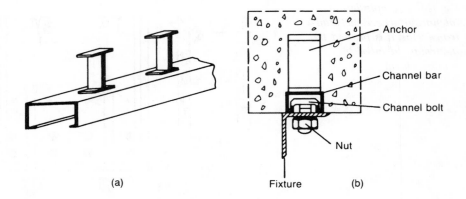

(a)  Fixture  (b)

*Fig. 10. Typical shear lug*

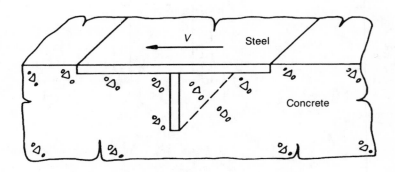

The Design Guide is valid for single anchors and anchor groups. In an anchor group the loads are applied to the individual anchors of the group by means of a common fixture. The arrangement of anchors covered by this Guide is given in the corresponding Part.

## 1.2. Anchor dimensions and steel strength

This Guide applies to anchors with a minimum thread size of 6 mm (M6) or a corresponding cross section. In general, the minimum anchorage depth should be 40 mm. The maximum steel tensile strength considered here is $f_{uk} = 100$ MPa.

This Guide does not cover fastenings in non-structural layers.

*Comment*

This minimum anchorage depth is limited to 40 mm based on the following considerations:

(1) Depending on reinforcement density and casting method and direction, the quality of the cover concrete can vary considerably.

(2) In general, to reduce stress concentration in the concrete it is preferable that the load-transfer zone of anchors loaded in tension be positioned beyond the innermost reinforcement layer as depicted in Fig. 11. As a rule, the load-transfer zone should extend at least beyond the outermost layer of the principle reinforcement. Consideration of typical cover requirements and reinforcement patterns leads to recommendation of a minimum anchorage depth of 40 mm.

In general, the bond between a non-structural layer (screeds and toppings, plaster) and concrete is rather poor. Therefore these layers may not be able to transfer anchor loads or to improve the resistance of the anchorage.

## 1.3. Anchor loading

This Design Guide applies to anchors subjected primarily to static loading and not to anchors subjected to dynamic loading. Certain types of anchors may also be subjected to cyclic loads which may cause fatigue failure. If so, this is stated explicitly in the following Parts. The fixture may be subjected

Fig. 11. Example of an
anchorage where the load-
transfer area is beyond the
innermost layer of
reinforcement

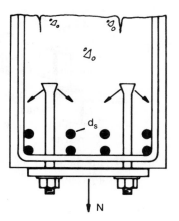

to tension, shear or combined tension and shear loads as well as bending and
torsion moments. The shear loads may also be applied with a lever arm
causing a bending moment in the anchors. Compression loads on a fixture
are allowed only if these loads are transferred from the fixture into the concrete without loading the anchors (see Fig. 12(a) and (b)) or if the anchors
are suitable to transfer compression loads (for example see Fig. 12(c)).

*Comment*
For dynamic loading (seismic, wind, blast loads etc.) the provisions given in
this Guide may be applied with engineering judgement. In general, the
increased strain rates associated with dynamic loads increase the capacities of
the constituent materials. However, other considerations, such as ductility
requirements, displacement limitations, load reversals, increased crack widths,
individual anchor characteristics etc., are not explicitly considered here. A
corresponding CEB Design Guide for anchorages subjected to dynamic loads
is in preparation.

In general, post-installed anchors should not be loaded by a compression
force, because then the anchor may slip back into the hole. Exceptions are
allowed for bonded anchors and certain types of undercut anchors.

### 1.4. Concrete strength

This Guide applies to members made of concrete with normal weight
aggregates of at least strength class C 20 and at most strength class C 50
according to CEB–FIP Model Code 1990 (MC 90).[1] In the region of the
fastening, the concrete may be cracked or non-cracked. In general, it is
assumed that the concrete is cracked; for exceptions, see section 5.

Fig. 12. Fastening loaded by
a bending moment and a
compression force: (a), (b),
anchors not loaded in
compression; in (a) the
compression force is taken up
by the fixture and in (b) by
the washer; (c) anchors
loaded in compression

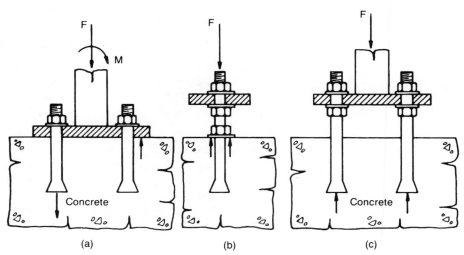

*Comment*
In the case of concrete with a strength less than about $20 \, N/mm^2$ local variations in concrete density and quality may lead to an unacceptable scatter in anchor load displacement behaviour and strength. The upper limit on concrete strength is derived from the following considerations:

(1) Some anchor types (e.g. expansion anchors) may exhibit poor performance in high-strength concrete.
(2) With higher concrete strength the equations given to calculate the resistance in the case of concrete failure may be unconservative.

The assumption that generally the concrete is cracked is conservative and a simplification.

## 1.5. Concrete member loading

In general, the concrete member should be subjected to predominantly static loading (no fatigue or dynamic loading). The use of certain types of anchors may be allowed for fatigue loading on the concrete member (see the following Parts).

*Comment*
Fatigue loading of cracked concrete members implies repeated cycles of crack openings and closings. These crack movements may negatively influence the anchor behaviour. Knowledge regarding the behaviour of the various anchor types under these conditions is rather limited.

## 1.6. Safety classes

In this Design Guide it is assumed that the fastenings belong to Safety Class 2 according to Ref. 4.

*Comment*
The provisions in Ref. 4 are based on the CEB International System of Unified Codes of Practice for Structures.[5] In Ref. 4 the safety classes are defined as shown in Table 1.

*Table 1. Safety classes according to Ref. 4*

| Possible consequences of failure | | Class |
|---|---|---|
| Mainly concerning ultimate bearing capacity | Mainly concerning serviceability* | |
| No risk to human life and economic consequence slight | Economic consequences slight and only slight impediment in use | 1 |
| Risk to human life exists and/or economic consequences considerable | Economic consequences considerable and considerable impediments in use | 2 |
| Structure of great public importance | Economic consequences great and severe impediments in use | 3 |

* If loss of serviceability entails risks to human life (e.g. leakage of vessels and pipes enclosing hazardous materials), this is treated as a loss of the ultimate bearing capacity.

For safety class 3 (e.g. fastenings in nuclear power plants), higher safety factors than given in this Guide and, in addition, more stringent criteria for checking the functions of the anchor and quality assurance procedures on site may be necessary.

In other countries different classifications may be used, e.g. in the USA the classification shown in Table 2 operates.

*Table 2. Classification of buildings and other structures for wind, snow and earthquake loads according to Ref. 6*

| Nature of occupancy | Category |
|---|---|
| All buildings and structures except those listed below | I |
| Buildings and structures where the primary occupancy is one in which more than 300 people congregate in one area | II |
| Buildings and structures designated as essential facilities, including but not limited for<br>(1) Hospital and other medical facilities having surgery or emergency treatment areas<br>(2) Fire or rescue and police stations<br>(3) Primary communication facilities and disaster operation centres<br>(4) Power stations and other utilities required in an emergency<br>(5) Structures having critical national defence capabilities | III |
| Buildings and structures that represent a low hazard to human life in the event of a failure, such as agricultural buildings, certain temporary facilities and minor storage facilities | IV |

The classification according to Table 2 corresponds approximately with the classes given in Table 1, as follows:

| Class according Table 1 | Classification according Table 2 |
|---|---|
| 1 | IV |
| 2 | I + II |
| 3 | III |

# 2. Terminology

The notation and symbols most frequently used in this Design Guide are listed below. Further notation is given in the text.

## 2.1. Indices

$S$ = action
$R$ = resistance
$M$ = material
$k$ = characteristic value
$d$ = design value
$s$ = steel
$c$ = concrete
$cp$ = concrete pry-out
$p$ = pull-out
$sp$ = splitting
$u$ = ultimate
$y$ = yield

## 2.2. Actions and resistances

$F$ = force in general
$N$ = normal force (positive = tension force, negative = compression force)
$V$ = shear force
$M$ = moment
$M_a$ = bending moment on anchor
$M_1$ = bending moment on fixture around axis in direction 1
$M_2$ = bending moment on fixture around axis in direction 2
$M_T$ = torsional moment on fixture

$F_{Sk}(N_{Sk}; V_{Sk}; M_{Sk}; M_{Sk,T})$ = characteristic value of actions acting on a single anchor or the fixture of an anchor group respectively (normal load; shear load; bending moment; torsion moment)

$F_{Sd}(N_{Sd}; V_{Sd}; M_{Sd}; M_{Sd,T})$ = design value of actions acting on a single anchor or the fixture of an anchor group respectively (normal load; shear load; bending moment; torsion moment)

$N_{Sd}^h(V_{Sd}^h)$ = design value of tensile load (shear load) acting on the most stressed anchor of an anchor group calculated according to Section 4.2.1.2

$N_{Sd}^g(V_{Sd}^g)$ = design value of the sum of the tensile (shear) loads acting on the tensioned (sheared) anchors of a group calculated according to Section 4.2.1.2 or 4.2.2.2 respectively

$F_{Rk}(N_{Rk}; V_{Rk})$ = characteristic value of resistance of a single anchor or an anchor group respectively (normal force; shear force)

$F_{Rd}(N_{Rd}; V_{Rd})$ = design value of resistance of a single anchor or an anchor group respectively (normal force; shear force)

*Comment*
The characteristic resistance is the 5% fractile of the resistance with a confidence level of 90%. It is that value, e.g. of a failure load, for which there is a 90% probability that it will be exceeded by 95% of the failure loads in the data population assuming an infinite number of test results.

### 2.3. Concrete and steel

$f_{ck}$ = characteristic compressive strength of concrete (strength class) measured on cylinders 150 mm × 300 mm according to MC 90.[1]

*Comment*
The curing of the cylinders must be done in accordance with MC 90.[1]

$f_{yk}$ = characteristic steel yield strength or steel proof strength respectively (nominal value)

$f_{uk}$ = characteristic steel ultimate tensile strength (nominal value)

$A_s$ = stressed cross-section of steel

$W_{el}$ = elastic section modulus calculated from the stressed cross-section of steel

### 2.4. Notation — dimensional

$a$ = spacing between outer anchors of adjoining groups or between outer anchors of a group and single anchors or between single anchors (see Fig. 13)

$a_1(a_2)$ = spacing between outer anchors of adjoining groups or between outer anchors of a group and single anchors or between single anchors in direction 1 (direction 2) (see Fig. 13)

$a_3$ = distance between concrete surface and point of assumed restraint of an anchor loaded by a shear force with lever arm (see Fig. 26(a))

$b$ = width of concrete member

$b_f$ = width of fixture

*Fig. 13. Definitions related to concrete member dimensions, anchor spacing and edge distance: (a) anchors subjected to tension load; (b) anchors subjected to shear load in the case of anchorage near an edge; indices 1 and 2 depend on the direction of the shear load (1, in direction of shear load; 2, perpendicular to direction of shear load)*

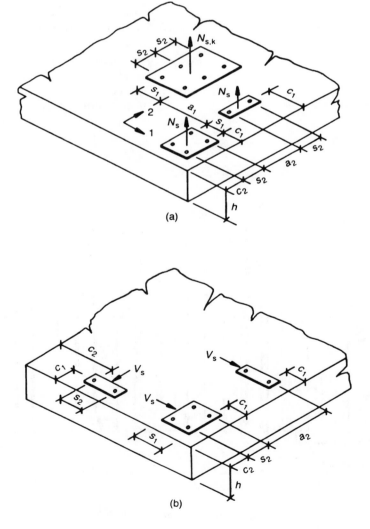

(a)

(b)

$c$ = edge distance from the axis of an anchor (see Fig. 13) or of a channel bar

$c_1$ = edge distance in direction 1; in the case of anchorages close to an edge loaded in shear, $c_1$ is the edge distance in the direction of the shear load (see Fig. 13(b))

$c_2$ = edge distance in direction 2; direction 2 is perpendicular to direction 1

$c_{cr,b}$ = edge distance necessary to develop the characteristic tension resistance of a single anchor without spacing, edge and member thickness effects in the case of concrete blow-out failure

$c_{cr,N}$ = edge distance necessary to develop the characteristic tension resistance of a single anchor without spacing and edge effects in the case of concrete cone failure

$c_{cr,sp}$ = edge distance necessary to ensure the transmission of the characteristic tension resistance for concrete cone failure of a single anchor without spacing and edge effects in the case of splitting failure

$c_{min}$ = minimum allowable edge distance

$d$ = diameter of anchor bolt or thread diameter

$d_c$ = diameter of clearance hole in the fixture

$d_h$ = diameter of anchor head (headed anchors)

$d_{nom}$ = outside diameter of anchor

$d_o$ = nominal diameter of drilled hole

$d_s$ = diameter of reinforcing bar

$d_1$ = diameter of undercut

$d_2$ = diameter of expanded undercut anchor

$e_1$ = distance between shear load and concrete surface (see Fig. 26)

$e_{N,e}(e_{V,e})$ = eccentricity of the external tension (shear) force in respect to the centre of gravity of a fastening (external eccentricity)

$e_N(e_V)$ = eccentricity of the resultant tension (shear) force of the tensioned (sheared) anchors in respect to the centre of gravity of the tensioned (sheared) anchors of a fastening (internal eccentricity)

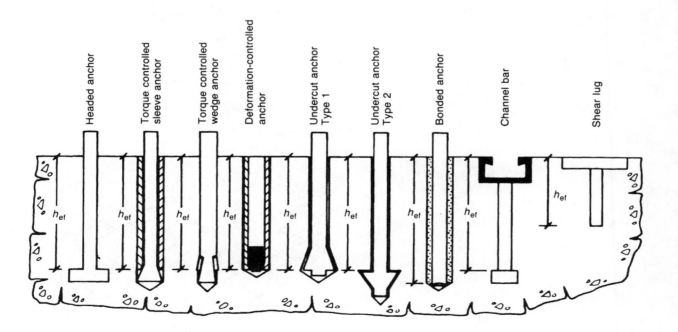

*Fig. 14. Definition of effective anchorage depth* $h_{ef}$

| | |
|---|---|
| $h$ | = thickness of anchorage member (see Fig. 13) |
| $h_{ef}$ | = effective anchorage depth (see Fig. 14) |
| $h_{min}$ | = minimum thickness of concrete member |
| $\ell$ | = lever arm of the shear force acting on an anchor |
| $\ell_f$ | = effective length of anchor under shear loading |
| $s$ | = centre-to-centre spacing of anchors in a group (see Fig. 13) or spacing of reinforcing bars |
| $s_1$ | = spacing of anchors in a group in direction 1 (see Fig. 13) |
| $s_2$ | = spacing of anchors in a group in direction 2 (see Fig. 13) |
| $s_{cr,b}$ | = spacing necessary to develop the characteristic tension resistance of a single anchor without spacing, edge and member thickness effects in the case of concrete blow-out failure |
| $s_{cr,N}$ | = spacing necessary to develop the characteristic tension resistance of a single anchor without spacing and edge effects in the case of concrete cone failure |
| $s_{cr,sp}$ | = spacing necessary to ensure the transmission of the characteristic tension resistance for concrete cone failure of a single anchor without spacing and edge effects in the case of splitting failure |
| $s_{min}$ | = minimum allowable spacing |

**2.5. Units**

In this document SI units are used. Unless stated otherwise in the equations the following units are used: dimensions are given in mm, cross-sections in $mm^2$, section modulus in $mm^3$, forces and loads in N and stresses in MPa.

# 3. Safety concept

## 3.1. General

For the design of fastenings the safety concept of partial safety factors according to the CEB–FIP Model Code 1990 is applied.[1] According to this concept, the values of the design actions $S_d$ should not exceed the value of the design resistance $R_d$.

$$S_d \leq R_d \tag{1}$$

where

$S_d$ = value of design actions of anchors

$R_d$ = value of design resistance of anchors

*Comment*
Figure 15(a) shows the frequency distributions of actions acting on a fixture and the resistances provided by the fastening. Failure will occur if the action on the fixture is greater than the resistance provided by the fastening. The probability of failure, $p_f$, is given by the failure density function (Fig. 15(b)). As a simplification, the area below the intersecting curves in Fig. 15(a) is a measure of the probability of failure. To ensure a sufficiently low probability of failure, adequate safety factors for actions and resistances are required. For a constant probability of failure, the material safety factor $\gamma_M$ depends on the scatter of the resistances.

The design actions in the ultimate limit state or serviceability limit state respectively should be calculated according to Ref. 1.

*Comment*
In the simplest case (permanent load and one variable load acting in the same direction as the permanent load) the following equation applies:

$$S_d = \gamma_G \cdot G_k + \gamma_Q \cdot Q_k \tag{2}$$

where

$G_k(Q_k)$ = characteristic value of permanent (variable) actions

$\gamma_G(\gamma_Q)$ = partial safety factor for permanent (variable) actions

For several variable actions, reduction factors for some variable actions might apply (see Ref. 1).

*Fig. 15. (a) Frequency distributions of actions on a fixture and resistances provided by the fastening; (b) failure density function, after Ref. 7*

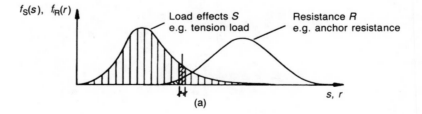

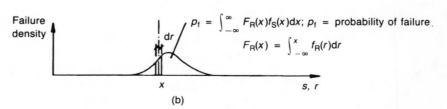

If deformations imposed to the fastened element (e.g. due to temperature variations) are restrained by the fastening, then the corresponding actions on the fastening ($Q_{ind}$) multiplied by an appropriate safety factor ($\gamma_{ind}$) should be added in equation (2).

## 3.2. Ultimate limit state of resistance

### 3.2.1. Design resistance
In the ultimate limit state of resistance, the value of the design resistance is obtained from the characteristic resistance of the anchor or anchor group respectively, as follows:

$$R_d = R_k/\gamma_M \tag{3}$$

where

$R_k$ = characteristic resistance of single anchor or anchor group, respectively (e.g. $N_{Rk}$ or $V_{Rk}$)
$\gamma_M$ = partial safety factor for material

*Comment*
The definition of the partial safety factor $\gamma_M$ is given in Ref. 8, section 6.3.2.

In several countries the characteristic resistance is multiplied by a strength reduction factor $\phi(\phi \le 1)$ instead of dividing it by a partial safety factor $\gamma_M(\gamma_M \ge 1)$. As an approximation, for a constant probability of failure, $\gamma$-factors can be converted into $\phi$-factors by equation (4),

$$\phi = \frac{\gamma_{f,2}}{\gamma_{f,1}\gamma_M} \tag{4}$$

with

$$\gamma_{f,1} = \frac{\gamma_G\left[1 + \dfrac{\gamma_Q \cdot Q_k}{\gamma_G \cdot G_k}\right]}{1 + Q_k/G_k} \tag{4a}$$

where

$G_k(Q_k)$ = characteristic value of permanent (variable) actions
$\gamma_G(\gamma_Q)$ = partial safety factor for permanent (variable) actions according to section 3.2.2
$\gamma_M$ = partial safety factor for materials according to section 3.2.3
$\gamma_{f,2}$ = partial safety factor for actions calculated according to equation (4a) inserting the factors $\gamma_G$ and $\gamma_Q$ associated with the design method using $\phi$-factors

Equation (4a) is valid for the simplest case (permanent load and one variable load). For more complicated loadings, equation (4a) should be modified accordingly.

### 3.2.2. Partial safety factors for actions
The partial safety factors for actions depend on the type of loading and should be taken from Ref. 1.

*Comment*
The partial safety factors for actions are independent of the materials used. In the absence of a generally accepted code for actions, they should be taken from Ref. 1.

In equation (2) in the case of unfavourable effects of actions the partial safety factor for permanent actions is $\gamma_G = 1.35$ and for variable actions $\gamma_Q = 1.50$.

The partial safety factor for actions, $Q_{ind}$, due to the restraint of imposed deformations of the fastened element may be taken as $\gamma_{ind} = 1.3$, if the characteristic resistance is governed by concrete failure. These actions may be neglected if the characteristic resistance is governed by ductile steel failure.

15

### 3.2.3. Partial safety factors for resistances

The material safety factors given in the following are valid for safety class 2 according to Ref. 4 (compare Table 1). Partial safety factors for safety classes 1 and 3 should be determined depending on the guidelines in each country.

*Comment*
The $\gamma_M$-factors are calibrated for the characteristic values of the materials.

### 3.2.3.1. Partial safety factors for concrete cone failure, concrete splitting failure, pull-out failure and friction.

The partial safety factors for concrete cone failure ($\gamma_{Mc}$), concrete splitting failure ($\gamma_{Msp}$), pull-out or pull-through failure ($\gamma_{Mp}$) and friction between fixture and concrete ($\gamma_{Mf}$) should be given in the relevant approval certificate or should be evaluated in the prequalification procedure. If not, the values given below may be used.

*Comment*
In case of pull-out failure the whole anchor is pulled out of the concrete. With torque-controlled expansion anchors the cone may be pulled through the sleeve (pull-through failure).

The partial safety factor $\gamma_{Mc}$ is determined from:

$$\gamma_{Mc} = \gamma_1 \cdot \gamma_2 \tag{5}$$

where

$\gamma_1$ = partial safety factor for concrete loaded in tension
    = 1.8
$\gamma_2$ = partial safety factor taking into account the uncertainties due to anchor installation (installation safety)

*Tension loading*
  $\gamma_2$ = 1.0 for systems with high installation safety
or $\gamma_2$ = 1.2 for systems with normal installation safety
or $\gamma_2$ = 1.4 for systems with low but still acceptable installation safety

*Shear loading*
  $\gamma_2$ = 1.0

*Comment*
The partial safety factor $\gamma_1$ is given by $\gamma_1 = 1.2\gamma_c$, where $\gamma_c = 1.5$ is the partial safety factor for concrete in compression and 1.2 is a modification factor taking into account that failure is caused by overcoming the concrete tension capacity.

The partial safety factor $\gamma_2$ (installation safety factor) depends on the fastening system. It is evaluated from the results of appropriate installation safety tests (e.g. according to Refs 9 to 11. As a first indication, the following values apply;

| | |
|---|---|
| Cast-in-place headed anchors, channel bars and most undercut anchors | $\gamma_2 = 1.0$ |
| Most torque-controlled expansion anchors | $\gamma_2 = 1.2$ |
| Most deformation-controlled expansion anchors | $\gamma_2 = 1.4$ |

The factors $\gamma_2$ given above or in the relevant approval certificate are valid only if after installation the actual values of the effective anchorage depth, spacing and edge distance are not less than the values used in the design (only positive tolerances are allowed on site).

*Comment*
Equation (5) is valid if the coefficient of variation of the failure loads is $V \leq 15\%$. If the coefficient of variation is $V > 15\%$, then equation (5) should be replaced by equation (5a):

$$\gamma_{Mc} = \gamma_1 \cdot \gamma_2 \cdot \gamma_3 \qquad (5a)$$

with $\gamma_1$, $\gamma_2$ as defined for equation (5) and

$$\gamma_3 = 1.0 + (V \, [\%] - 15) \times 0.03$$
$$\geq 1.0 \qquad (5b)$$

The factor $\gamma_3$ takes into account the scatter of the failure loads (resistance). Note that according to Ref. 10, a coefficient of variation $V > 15\%$ is, in general, not allowed for post-installed anchors. In any case, the coefficient of variations of the failure loads should be $V \lesssim 30\%$.

Unless otherwise stated in the following Parts, the partial safety factor for concrete splitting failure and for pull-out failure is taken as equal to the value for concrete cone failure ($\gamma_{Msp} = \gamma_{Mp} = \gamma_{Mc}$).

The partial safety factor for friction between fixture and concrete may be taken as $\gamma_{Mf} = 1.5$.

*3.2.3.2. Partial safety factors for steel failure.* The partial safety factor $\gamma_{Ms}$ for steel failure should be given in the relevant approval certificate or should be evaluated in the prequalification procedure. If not, the following values may be used.

*Tension loading*
$$\gamma_{Ms} = 1.20 \qquad (6a)$$

*Shear loading with and without lever arm*
$$\gamma_{Ms} = 1.20 \qquad f_{uk} \leq 800 \, \text{MPa and } f_{yk}/f_{uk} \leq 0.8 \qquad (6b)$$
$$\gamma_{Ms} = 1.50 \qquad f_{uk} > 800 \, \text{MPa or } f_{yk}/f_{uk} > 0.8 \qquad (6c)$$

*Comment*
An ASTM steel with a strength $f_{uk} \sim 800 \, \text{MPA}$ (e.g. $f_{uk} = 120\,000 \, psi = 830 \, \text{MPa}$) and $f_{yk}/f_{uk} \leq 0.8$ may be considered as 8.8-steel with $\gamma_{Ms} = 1.2$.

If in some Design Guides the characteristic resistance is based on $f_{uk}$ (e.g. as in Ref. 10, Annex C) and not on $f_{yk}$ as in this Guide, the values for $\gamma_{Ms}$ should be less than given above so that the design resistances are approximately equal in both cases.

## 3.3. Ultimate limit state of fatigue

In the ultimate limit state of fatigue, equations (1) to (3) are valid. The partial safety factor for actions ($\gamma_G$, $\gamma_Q$, $\gamma_{ind}$) may be taken as $\gamma_G = \gamma_Q = \gamma_{ind} = 1.1$. The partial safety factor for material should be taken as $\gamma_{Ms} = 1.25$ (steel failure), $\gamma_{Mc} = \gamma_{Msp} = \gamma_{Mp} = 1.5 \cdot \gamma_2$ [for $\gamma_2$ see equation (5)] (concrete cone failure, splitting failure and pull-out failure) and $\gamma_{Mf} = 1.2$ (friction).

*Comment*
Using the partial safety factors valid for the ultimate limit state (see section 3.2), no fatigue concrete cone failure will occur during $n \leq 2 \times 10^6$ load cycles.

The value $\gamma_{Ms} = 1.25$ for steel failure is valid for the characteristic strength at the endurance limit.

## 3.4. Serviceability limit state

In the serviceability limit state, equations (1) to (3) are valid also. Usually the partial safety factors for actions and resistances $\gamma_G$, $\gamma_Q$, $\gamma_{ind}$ and $\gamma_M$ are assumed to be equal to 1.0.

In the serviceability limit state, it should be shown that the displacements occurring under the design actions are not greater than the admissible displacement. The displacements occurring under the design actions should be evaluated according to the following Parts. The admissible displacement depends on the application in question, e.g. the structural element to be fastened, and should be evaluated by the designer.

*Comment*
It may also be necessary to limit the rotation of the fixture, if excessive rotations could lead to cosmetic or other non-structural damage.

The resultant stress in the most loaded anchor under the design tension and shear actions should not exceed 80% of the characteristic resistance of a single anchor in tension or shear, respectively.

*Comment*
If the design is performed according to the elastic design approach, this condition may be taken as satisfied by applying the proposed safety factors in the ultimate limit state for actions and steel failure.

If the design is performed according to the plastic design approach, then the check described above may be necessary.

## 3.5. Durability

The durability of a fastening assembly should not be less than the intended period of use of the connection or of the section of the building for which the assembly is required. For this period of use, the mechanical properties of the fastening assembly should not be adversely affected by physico-chemical influences such as corrosion, oxidation, aging or alkalinity of the concrete.

The anchorage and its protection should be selected in accordance with the environmental conditions at the place of installation. It should be borne in mind that there may be an adverse change in the environmental conditions over the period of use (e.g. corrosion as a result of industrialization) and the anchorages cannot, in general, be inspected and maintained.

Detailed conditions to ensure durable anchorages are given in the corresponding Parts of this Guide.

*Comment*
In general, the intended period of use is assumed to be 50 years for buildings.

# 4. Determination of action effects

## 4.1. General

When calculating the design actions on the fixture, the actions due to an eventual restraint of deformations imposed on the fastened element (e.g. due to temperature variations) by the fastening should be taken into account.

*Comment*
In general, when calculating the actions on the fixture, the displacement of the anchors is neglected. However, when a statically indeterminate stiff structure is fastened, then the effect of anchor displacements may be significant and should be considered in the calculation of the actions on the fixture and on the fastened component.

When a bending moment and/or a compression force is acting on a fixture in direct contact with concrete or mortar (Fig. 16) a friction force may develop, which for simplicity may conservatively be neglected in the design of the anchorage. If it is to be taken into account, then the design value of this friction force may be taken as

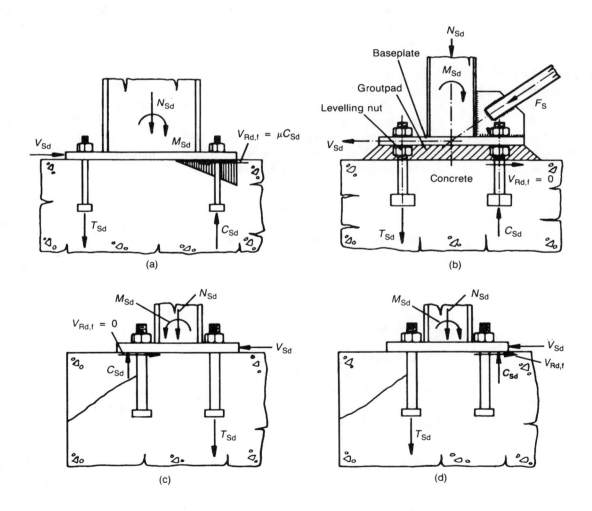

*Fig. 16. Friction force due to a resulting compression reaction on the fixture: (a), (d), friction force may be considered in the design; (b), (c), friction force should not be considered in the design*

$$V_{Rd,f} = V_{Rk,f}/\gamma_{Mf} = \mu \cdot C_{Sd}/\gamma_{Mf} \qquad (7)$$

with

$\mu$ = coefficient of friction
$C_{Sd}$ = compression force under the fixture due to the design actions
$\gamma_{Mf}$ = 1.5 (ultimate limit state)
or $\gamma_{Mf}$ = 1.3 (limit state of fatigue)
or $\gamma_{Mf}$ = 1.0 (serviceability limit state)

*Comment*
In general, the coefficient of friction between a fixture and concrete may be taken as $\mu = 0.4$.

The friction force $V_{Rd,f}$ should be neglected if the thickness of mortar beneath the fixture is >3 mm (e.g. in case of levelling nuts) (see Fig. 16(b)) and for anchorages close to an edge (see Fig. 16(c)).

*Comment*
If the friction force calculated by equation (7) is taken into account in the design, usually in the elastic design approach it is subtracted from the shear force acting on the fixture and in the plastic design approach it is added to the design shear resistance of the fastening.

For anchorages close to an edge it is generally assumed that the edge failure starts from the anchors closest to the edge. The resistance of the anchorage is increased if the friction force is acting on the side of the fixture furthest away from the edge (Fig. 16(d)) but is not influenced by a friction force acting on the failed concrete (Fig. 16(c)).

## 4.2. Ultimate limit state of resistance

Starting from the given action effects on the fixture (loads, bending and torsion moments), the action effects (tension and shear forces and, in case of a stand-off installation, shear force with lever arm) on each anchor should be calculated using the partial safety factors for actions according to section 3.2.2. In general, this calculation may be based on linear elastic material behaviour. It may also be based on plastic material behaviour if the conditions given in section 4.2.2.1 are met.

*Comment*
It may also be necessary to check the connection rotation for conformance with the analysis of the attached structure. For example, if the analysis assumes fixity at the connection, care must be taken that the calculated rotations resulting from the design of the connection are acceptable for the attached structure. This is especially valid if the design of the fastening is based on the plastic analysis. Likewise, an assumption of zero fixity at the connection can only be true if measures are taken to ensure this condition in the detailing, and may otherwise lead to an unconservative design, particularly with regard to the anchors.

### 4.2.1. Elastic analysis
In general, the action effects on an anchor at the concrete surface may be calculated according to an elastic analysis from the action effects on the fixture. The use of this method is compulsory when the expected mode of failure is brittle.

*Comment*
A brittle failure may be assumed in the case of concrete break-out, splitting failure or rupture of steel with insufficient ductility. The required ductility is determined by the degree of load redistribution assumed in the analysis. For example, in a plastic analysis, the ductility must be sufficient to accommodate yielding of all anchors on the tension side. In the case of ductile behaviour of the anchorage, the elastic design approach is conservative.

*4.2.1.1. Field of application.* The field of application for the different types of anchors is given in subsequent Parts. In one anchor group only anchors of the same type, size and length should be used.

*4.2.1.2. Tension loads on anchors.* The tension loads acting on each anchor due to loads and bending moments acting on the fixture may be calculated according to beam theory using the following assumptions.

(a) The fixture does not deform under the design actions.

*Comment*
This assumption is valid only if the fixture is rigid and in full contact with the concrete or with a layer of mortar. The fixture may be assumed to be rigid, if the maximum steel stress in the fixture under the design actions is smaller than $f_{sd} \leq f_{yk}/\gamma_{Ms}$ with $\gamma_{Ms} = 1.1$. When calculating the stresses in the fixture by an elastic analysis the stresses averaged over twice the fixture thickness may be taken as decisive. If a simplified analysis is carried out, conservative assumptions should be made.

Flexible fixtures may be used if the resultant non-linear load distribution and associated prying forces are taken into account (see Fig. 17). This case is not considered further here.

(b) The stiffness of all anchors is equal. It should be taken as the average steel stiffness along the embedment depth.

The modulus of elasticity of the concrete may be taken from Ref. 1.

*Comment*
As a simplification, the modulus of elasticity of concrete may be taken as $E_c = 30\,000\,\text{MPa}$.

(c) In the zone of compression under the fixture, the anchors do not contribute to the transmission of tension forces.

*Comment*
The assumptions (a)–(c) are shown in Fig. 18 for an anchorage loaded by a bending moment. The assumption of a rigid fixture is equivalent to the Bernoulli hypothesis of plane sections used in the analysis of reinforced concrete members.

For anchor groups with different levels of tension forces $N_{si}$ acting on the individual anchors of a group the eccentricity $e_N$ of the tension force $N_S^g$ of the group may be calculated (see Fig. 19).

*Fig. 17. Example of an anchorage with a flexible fixture loaded by a bending moment and a tension force*

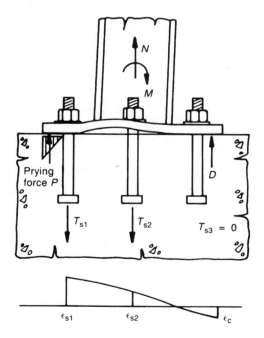

*Fig. 18. Example of an anchorage with a rigid fixture loaded by a bending moment and a normal force*

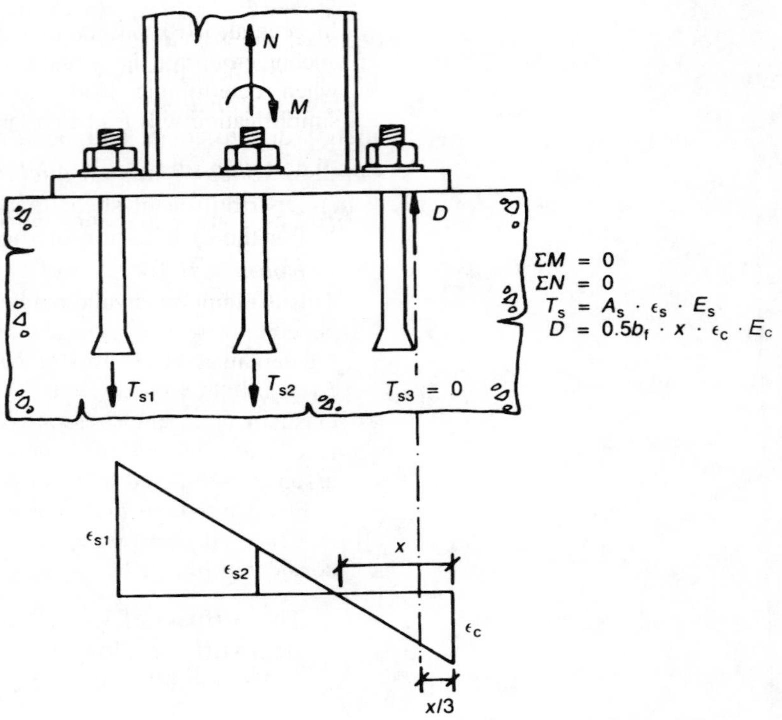

$$\Sigma M = 0$$
$$\Sigma N = 0$$
$$T_s = A_s \cdot \epsilon_s \cdot E_s$$
$$D = 0.5b_f \cdot x \cdot \epsilon_c \cdot E_c$$

*Fig. 19. Examples of anchorages subjected to an eccentric tensile load $N_S$: (a) eccentricity in one direction — all anchors are loaded by a tension force; (b) eccentricity in one direction — only some of the anchors of the group are loaded by a tension force; (c) eccentricity in two directions — only some of the anchors of the group are loaded by a tension force*

$$N_s^g = \Sigma N_{si}$$
$$N_{s1} = N_s^h$$

(a)

$$N_s^g = \Sigma N_{si}$$
$$N_{s1} = N_s^h$$

(b)

- Tensile anchors
⊕ Centre of gravity of tensile anchors
✗ Point of resulting tensile force of tensile anchors

(c)

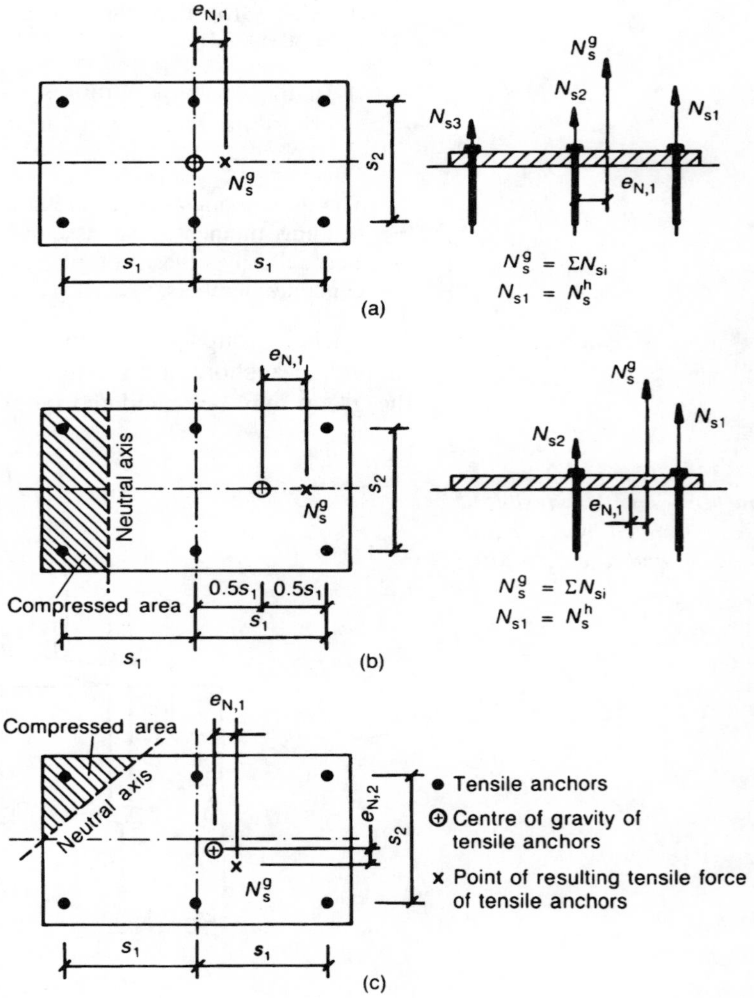

*Comment*

In general, it is conservative to substitute the centre of gravity of the entire anchor group for the actual centre of gravity of the anchors loaded in tension when determining load eccentricity (e.g. in Figs 19(b) and 19(c) this simplification will lead to a larger eccentricity).

### 4.2.1.3. Shear loads on anchors.

(*a*) Distribution of shear loads

For the distribution of shear loads to the anchors in a group resulting from shear forces and torsional moments acting on the fixture, the following cases should be distinguished.

(1) All anchors in the group are assumed to participate in carrying shear loads if the following conditions are met:

    (i)  the edge distance is sufficiently large to ensure steel failure of the anchor; and

    (ii)  the anchors are welded to or threaded into the fixture; or in the case of anchorages with a clearance hole in the fixture, the diameter of the clearance hole is $d_c \leq 1.2d$ (the bolt is assumed to bear against the fixture; see Fig. 20(a)), or $d_c \leq 1.2d_{nom}$ (the sleeve is assumed to bear against the fixture; see Fig. 20(b)).

Examples for the resulting load distributions are shown in Fig. 21.

(2) Only those anchors having the least calculated resistance (e.g. due to positioning and/or to combined loading) are assumed to carry shear loads when either of the following conditions are met:

    (i)  the edge distance is small so that concrete edge failure will

*Fig. 20. Examples of anchorages with a large edge distance with a clearance hole in the fixture where all anchors will contribute to the transmission of shear forces: (a) the bolt is assumed to bear against fixture; (b) the sleeve is assumed to bear against fixture*

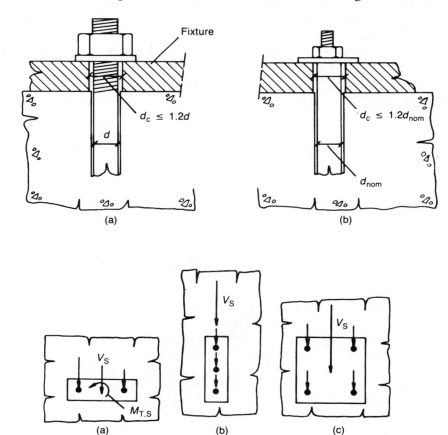

*Fig. 21. Examples of load distribution, when all the anchors take up shear load*

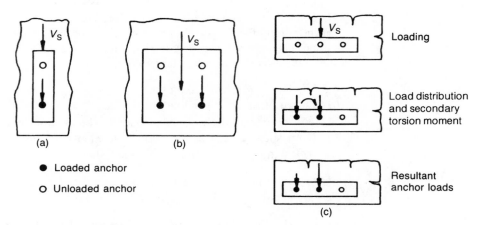

Fig. 22. *Examples of load distribution for anchorages close to an edge or corner of the concrete member*

Fig. 23. *Examples of load distribution if the hole clearance is large*

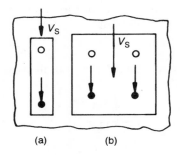

occur and steel failure of the anchors will be procluded, independent of the hole clearance; or

(ii) the hole clearance is large ($d_c > 1.2d$, $d_c > 1.2d_{nom}$ — refer to Figs 20(a) and 20(b), respectively), independent of the edge distance.

Anchor load distributions for each of these cases are shown in Figs 22 and 23, respectively.

Note that in cases where two anchors in a group are loaded by a shear force acting perpendicular to the group axis and/or by a torsional moment, both anchors can be assumed to carry load (see Fig. 21(a)), independent of edge distance and hole clearance.

In the case of a group of three or more anchors, the load should be conservatively distributed to only two anchors of the group. As demonstrated in Fig. 22(c), the assumed load distribution results in a secondary torsion moment which must be distributed to the anchors of the group in such a way as to satisfy equilibrium.

(3) The positioning of slotted holes in the fixture parallel to the direction of the shear load can be used to prevent particular anchors in the group from carrying load. This method can be used to relieve anchors close to an edge which would otherwise cause a premature edge failure (see Fig. 24).

*Comment*
When there is a clearance hole in the fixture, in general a shear load will not be equally distributed to all anchors of a group, because some anchors may already be loaded almost to failure before other anchors come into contact with the fixture, e.g. if the hole clearance is large (see Fig. 23). This is especially valid for anchorages close to an edge (see Fig. 22), because they may fail at rather small displacements. To account for this, it should be assumed that only the most unfavourable anchors take up load. This assumption is on the safe side.

For anchors welded, friction-bolted or otherwise securely attached to the fixture, concrete failure will initially occur in the anchors closest to the free edge, and the peak load will be reached when concrete break-out is initiated in the anchor(s) furthest from the edge. If the anchor spacing is small, the load increase associated with the failure of the anchor(s) furthest from the edge may be small. Furthermore, the premature failure of the anchor(s) closest to the edge may negatively influence the behaviour of the structural member or cause serviceability problems. For this reason, it is suggested that the calculation of the capacity of the group should be based solely on the capacity of the

*Fig. 24. Example of load distribution for an anchorage with slotted holes*

● Loaded anchor

○ Unloaded anchor

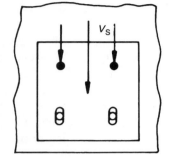

anchor(s) closest to the edge and only those anchors should be assumed to take up shear loads (see Fig. 22).

In the case of an anchorage according to Fig. 21(a) with a clearance hole in the fixture, after a displacement of the fixture both anchors will come into contact with the fixture and will take up a shear load.

Slotted holes (Fig. 24) will often be used for anchorages close to an edge to prevent the anchors closest to the edge from taking up shear loads.

In the case of anchor groups with different levels of shear forces $V_{si}$ acting on the individual anchors of the group, the eccentricity $e_v$ of the shear force $V_S^g$ of the group may be calculated (see Fig. 25).

(*b*) Shear loads without lever arm
Shear loads acting on anchors may be assumed to act without a lever arm if both of the following conditions are fulfilled.

(1) The fixture must be made of metal and in the area of the anchorage be fixed directly to the concrete without an intermediate layer or with a levelling layer of mortar with a thickness $\leq 3$ mm.
(2) The fixture must be adjacent to the anchor over its entire thickness.

*Fig. 25. Example of an anchorage subjected to an eccentric shear load*

⊕ Centre of gravity of sheared anchors
✗ Point of resulting shear force of sheared anchors

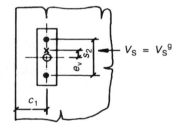

*Comment*
The influence of the diameter of the clearance hole is taken into account in the calculation of the distribution of shear loads to the anchors (see Figs 21 and 23). Therefore the above conditions are valid also for a large diameter of the clearance hole.

(*c*) Shear loads with lever arm
If the conditions (1) and (2) of the immediately preceding section (*b*) are not fulfilled, the length $\ell$ of the lever arm is calculated according to equation (8):

$$\ell = a_3 + e_1 \tag{8}$$

with

$e_1$ = distance between shear load and concrete surface
$a_3$ = 0.5d for post-installed and cast-in-place anchors (see Fig. 26(a))
or $a_3$ = 0 if a washer and a nut are directly clamped to the concrete surface (see Fig. 26(b))
$d$ = nominal diameter of the anchor bolt or thread diameter (see Fig. 26(a))

*Fig. 26. Lever arm*

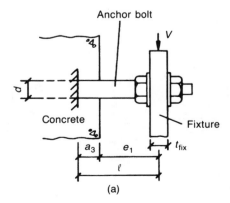

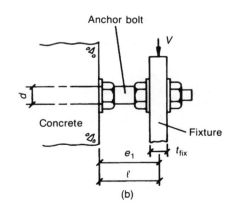

The design moment acting on the anchor is calculated according to equation (9):

$$M_{Sd} = V_{Sd} \cdot \frac{\ell}{\alpha_M} \tag{9}$$

The value of $\alpha_M$ depends on the degree of restraint of the anchor at the side of the fixture of the application in question, and should be determined according to good engineering practice.

No restraint ($\alpha_M = 1.0$) should be assumed if the fixture can rotate freely (see Fig. 27(a)). This assumption is always on the safe side.

Full restraint ($\alpha_M = 2.0$) may be assumed only if the fixture cannot rotate (see Fig. 27(b)) and the hole clearance in the fixture is smaller than $1.2d$ (the bolt is assumed to bear against the fixture; see Fig. 20(a)) or $1.2d_{nom}$ (the sleeve is assumed to bear against the fixture; see Fig. 20(b)), respectively, or the fixture is clamped to the anchor by a nut and a washer (see Fig. 26). If restraint of the anchor is assumed, the fixture and/or the fastened element must be able to take up the restraint moment.

### 4.2.2. Plastic analysis

#### 4.2.2.1. Field of application.
In a plastic analysis it is assumed that significant redistribution of anchor tension and shear forces will occur in a group. Therefore, this analysis is acceptable only when the failure is governed by ductile steel failure of the anchor.

*Comment*
Pull-out or pull-through failure may occur at large displacements allowing for some redistribution of tension forces. However, there may not be a significant redistribution of shear forces. In view of the lack of information on the required behaviour, a plastic analysis should not be used for this type of failure.

To ensure a ductile steel failure, the following conditions should be met:

(1) Anchor arrangements shown in Fig. 28 are allowed. The fixture may be loaded by normal and shear forces and by a bending moment around one axis.

*Comment*
Other forms of the attachment are possible too. The number of anchors parallel to the axis of bending might be larger than two.

(2) The ultimate strength of a fastening as governed by concrete failure should exceed its strength as governed by steel failure (equation (10)):

$$R_{d,c} \geq 1.25 R_{d,s} \cdot f_{uk}/f_{yk} \tag{10}$$

with

*Fig. 27. Examples of fastenings (a) without and (b) with full restraint of the anchor at the side of the fixture*

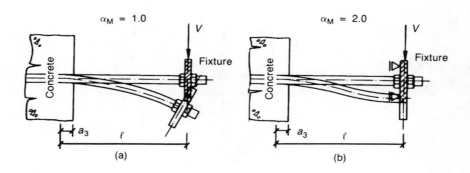

*Fig. 28. Anchor arrangements for which the plastic design approach may be used*

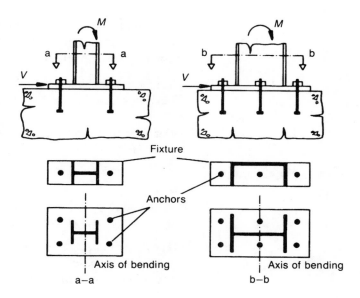

$R_{d,c}$ = design concrete capacity of the fastening (concrete cone, splitting or pull-out failure (tension loading) or concrete pry-out or edge failure (shear loading))

$R_{d,s}$ = design steel capacity of the fastening

Equation (10) should be checked for tension, shear and combined tension and shear forces on the anchors.

(3) The nominal steel strength of the anchors should not exceed $f_{uk} \sim$ 800 MPa, the ratio of nominal steel yield strength to nominal ultimate strength should not exceed $f_{yk}/f_{uk} = 0.8$, and the rupture elongation (measured over a length equal to $5d$) should be at least 12%.

*Comment*
ASTM A193 B7 steel may be assumed to fulfil the above requirements.

(4) Anchors that incorporate a reduced section (e.g. a threaded part) should satisfy the following conditions.

(a) For anchors loaded in tension, the strength $N_{uk}$ of the reduced section should either be greater than 1.1 times the yield strength $N_{yk}$ of the unreduced section, or the stressed length of the reduced section should be $\geq 5d$ ($d$ = anchor diameter outside reduced section).

(b) For anchors loaded in shear or which are to redistribute shear forces, the beginning of the reduced section should either be $\geq 5d$ below the concrete surface or in the case of threaded anchors the threaded part should extend $\geq 2d$ into the concrete.

(c) For anchors loaded in combined tension and shear, the conditions (a) and (b) above should be met.

(5) The steel fixture should be embedded in the concrete or fastened to the concrete without an intermediate layer or with a layer of mortar with a thickness of $\leq 3$ mm.

(6) The diameter of the clearance hole in the fixture should be $\leq 1.2d$ (the bolt is assumed to bear against fixture; see Fig. 20(a)) or $\leq 1.2d_{nom}$ (the sleeve is assumed to bear against fixture; see Fig. 20(b)), respectively.

*4.2.2.2. Loads on anchors.* It may be assumed that all anchors are stressed up to their design resistance without taking compatibility conditions into account. However, the following conditions should be met.

(1) Tension and shear acting on each anchor should lie within the tension–shear interaction diagram for that anchor (compare section 9.4).

(2) For design purposes, the compressive stress between fixture and concrete may be assumed to be a rectangular stress block with $\sigma_c = 4f_{ck}$.

*Comment*

$\sigma_c = 4f_{ck}$ corresponds to the maximum value according to MC 90 for partial loading.[1] This assumed stress distribution is indicated in Figs 29 and 30.

(3) The location of the resultant compressive force $C_{Sd}$ should be determined based on rigid or flexible baseplate behaviour in accordance with (*a*) and (*b*) below.

*Comment*

For both rigid and flexible baseplate behaviour, the distribution of compressive stresses between the base plate and concrete is highly indeterminate. The actual distribution depends on the surface conditions of both the concrete and the baseplate.

(*a*) Rigid baseplate behaviour: for a rigid baseplate behaviour the compressive force is assumed to occur at the extreme edge of the baseplate as shown in Fig. 29. For rigid baseplate behaviour to occur, the baseplate must be of sufficient thickness to prevent yielding of the fixture at the edge of the attached member on the compression side of the fixture. The minimum baseplate thickness may be determined by satisfying equation (11)

$$M_{yd} > C_{Sd} \cdot a_4 \tag{11}$$

with

$M_{yd}$ = design moment that causes yielding of the fixture cal-culated from $f_{yd} = f_{yk}/\gamma_{Ms}$ ($\gamma_{Ms}$ may be taken as 1.1)
$C_{Sd}$ = design resultant compressive force
$a_4$ = distance from the edge of the attached member to the resultant compressive force

(*b*) Flexible baseplate behaviour: if the baseplate is not stiff enough to obtain rigid baseplate behaviour, a hinge will form on the compression side of the baseplate at the edge of the attached member. This will cause the compressive reaction to move

*Fig. 29. Rigid baseplate behaviour*

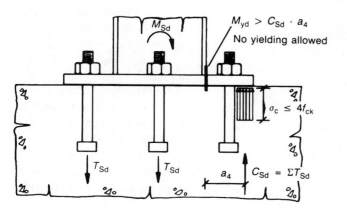

*Fig. 30. Flexible baseplate
behaviour*

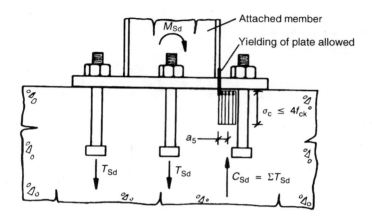

inward, towards the attached member. The distance $a_5$ between the edge of the attached member and the resultant of the compressive reaction may be calculated according to equation (12) (see Fig. 30).

$$a_5 = \frac{M_{yd}}{C_{Sd}} \tag{12}$$

with $M_{yd}$ and $C_{Sd}$ as defined in equation (11).

*Comment*
Equation (12) assumes a known baseplate thickness. It determines the maximum internal lever arm.

Conservatively, many designers will assume that the compressive reaction is located at either the edge ($a_5 = 0$) or the centroid of the compression element of the attached member. This simplifies design calculation since the thickness of the baseplate does not need to be known initially.

(4) For both cases (rigid baseplate behaviour and flexible baseplate behaviour), the formation of a hinge in the baseplate on the tension side of the connection must be prevented. This is necessary to ensure that prying action between the baseplate and the concrete does not develop (compare Fig. 17). Prying action may be prevented by satisfying equation (13).

$$M_{yd} > T_{sd} \cdot a_6 \tag{13}$$

with $M_{yd}$ as defined in equation (11) and
$T_{Sd}$ = sum of the design tension forces of the outermost row of anchors
$a_6$ = distance between outermost tension anchors and edge of the attached numbers (see Fig. 31)

*Fig. 31. Prevention of prying
action*

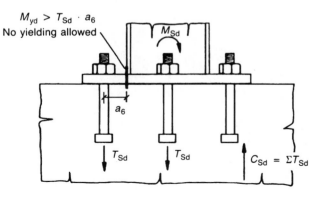

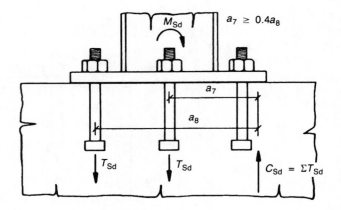

*Fig. 32. Condition for anchors transferring a tension force equal to the yield force*

*Comment*
Equation (13) is valid for one row of anchors outside the fixture.

(5) Only those fasteners which satisfy equation (14) should be assumed to transfer a tension force (see Fig. 32).

$$a_7 \geq 0.4a_8 \tag{14}$$

with

$a_7(a_8) =$ distance between the resultant compression force and the innermost (outermost) tensioned anchor

(6) It may be assumed that all anchors or only some of the anchors carry shear loads. The shear load taken by the individual anchors of a group may be different.

*Comment*
With a plastic design approach, the area of anchor steel may be reduced in comparison with an elastic design approach. However, the required anchorage depth and edge distance may be larger than for the elastic design approach, to preclude a concrete failure.

## 4.3. Ultimate limit state of fatigue and serviceability limit state

In the ultimate limit state of fatigue and the serviceability limit state, the loads acting on the anchors at the concrete surface should be calculated according to the elastic analysis (see section 4.2.1) from the loads and moments acting on the fixture, using the partial safety factors for actions given in sections 3.3 and 3.4, respectively.

# 5. Non-cracked concrete

Non-cracked concrete may be assumed in the design of anchorages if in each individual case it is shown that in the serviceability limit state the anchor with its entire anchorage depth is situated in non-cracked concrete. Non-cracked concrete is assumed to be verified if equation (15) is observed:

$$\sigma_L + \sigma_R \leq 0 \tag{15}$$

$\sigma_L$ = stresses in the concrete induced by external loads including anchor loads

$\sigma_R$ = stresses in the concrete due to restraint of intrinsic imposed deformations (e.g. shrinkage of concrete) or extrinsic imposed deformations (e.g. due to displacement of support or temperature variations); if no detailed analysis is conducted, then $\sigma_R = 3\,\text{MPa}$ should be assumed

The stresses $\sigma_L$ and $\sigma_R$ should be calculated assuming that the concrete is non-cracked. For slabs, walls and shells equation (15) should be checked for both mutually perpendicular directions in the plane of the structure.

# 6. General requirements for a method to calculate the design resistance of a fastening

The characteristic resistance of an anchorage should be based on the computation or test evaluation of the steel tensile and shear resistances, the concrete break-out tensile and shear resistances, the concrete splitting resistance and the tensile pull-out resistance of the anchors. The characteristic resistance is defined as the 5% fractile of the strength of the total population for a confidence level of 90%. The minimum of the above-mentioned resistances divided by the appropriate partial safety factor for resistance (see section 3.2.3) should be taken as the design resistance. For combined tension and shear forces their interaction on the resistance should be taken into account.

*Comment*
In codes, the nominal steel yield strength and nominal steel ultimate strength are often given. These nominal values may be assumed to be characteristic values.

The characteristic concrete break-out tensile resistance and characteristic concrete break-out shear resistance for any anchor should be based on design models which result in prediction of strength in substantial agreement with the results of comprehensive tests, and which account for size effects. The models should take into account factors which effect anchor strength such as anchorage depth, spacing, edge distance, depth of the structural member, and the presence or the absence of concrete cracking. Limits on edge distance and anchor spacing in the design model should be consistent with the tests which have verified the model. Interaction of tensile and shear loads should be considered in design using an interaction expression which results in prediction of strength in substantial agreement with the results of comprehensive tests.

*Comment*
The above requirements are satisfied by the Concrete Capacity Method (CC-Method) described in the following Parts of this Guide.

# 7. Provisions for ensuring the characteristic resistance of the concrete member

## 7.1. General

The local transmission of the anchor loads to the concrete is checked according to equation (1). The characteristic resistance of the anchorage is given in the following Parts of this Design Guide.

The transmission of the anchor loads to the supports of the concrete member should be checked for the ultimate limit state and the serviceability limit state according to the usual verifications, with due consideration of the anchor loads. For these verifications the additional provisions given in sections 7.2 and 7.3 should be taken into account.

## 7.2. Shear resistance of concrete member

In general, the shear forces $V_{\text{Sd,a}}$ induced in the concrete member by anchor loads should not exceed the value

$$V_{\text{Sd,a}} = 0.4 V_{\text{Rdl}} \tag{16}$$

with

$V_{\text{Rdl}}$ = shear resistance according to MC 90, equation (6.4–8)[1]

When calculating $V_{\text{Sd,a}}$ the anchor loads are to be assumed to be point loads with a width of load application $t_1 = s_{t1} + 2h_{\text{ef}}$ and $t_2 = s_{t2} + 2h_{\text{ef}}$ with $s_{t1}(s_{t2})$ = distance between the outermost anchors of a group in direction 1 (2). The active width over which the shear force is transmitted should be calculated according to the theory of elasticity.

*Comment*
Aids for calculating the active width are given in textbooks, e.g. in Ref. 12.

Equation (16) may be neglected if one of the following conditions is met.

(a) The anchorage depth of the anchor is

$$h_{\text{ef}} \geq 0.8h \tag{17}$$

(b) The shear force $V_{\text{Sd}}$, acting on the member at the support caused by the design actions including the actions on the fastenings, is

$$V_{\text{Sd}} \leq 0.8 V_{\text{Rdl}} \tag{18}$$

with $V_{\text{Rdl}}$ as defined in equation (16)

(c) Under the characteristic actions, the tension force $N_{\text{Sk}}$ of a single anchor, or the resultant tension force $N_{\text{Sk}}^{\text{g}}$ of the tensioned anchors of an anchor group, respectively, is smaller than 30 kN and the spacing $a$ between the outer anchors of adjacent groups, or between the outer anchors of a group and single anchors, or between single anchors, satisfies equation (19):

$$a \geq 200 N_{\text{Sk}}^{\,0.5} \quad \text{for single anchors} \tag{19a}$$

$$a \geq 200 (N_{\text{Sk}}^{\text{g}})^{0.5} \quad \text{for anchor groups} \tag{19b}$$

with $a$ in mm and $N_{\text{Sk}}$ in kN.

*Comment*
In equation (19) the constant is in the units mm/kN$^{0.5}$.

(d) The anchor loads are taken up by hanger reinforcement which

33

*Fig. 33. Example of an
anchorage with hanger
reinforcement to transfer the
loads to the opposite side of
the concrete member:
(a) longitudinal section;
(b) cross-section*

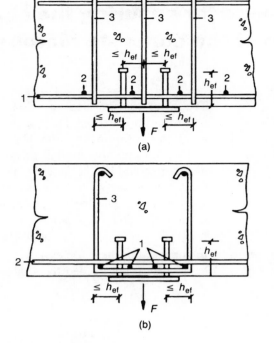

(a)

1 Main tension
  reinforcement
2 Secondary
  reinforcement
3 Hanger
  reinforcement

(b)

encloses the tension reinforcement and is anchored at the opposite side of the concrete member. The distance from any anchor to the hanger reinforcement should not be larger than $h_{ef}$ (see Fig. 33). At least two stirrups should be provided.

If, under the characteristic actions, the tension force $N_{Sk}$ of a single anchor, or the resultant tension force $N_{Sk}^g$ of the tensioned anchors of an anchor group, respectively, is larger than 60 kN, then either the anchorage depth of the anchors should be $h_{ef} \geq 0.8h$ or a hanger reinforcement according to paragraph (*d*) above should be provided.

*Comment*
The provisions given in this section are deduced for reinforced concrete members without shear reinforcement. They are conservative for members with shear reinforcement.

Hanger reinforcement may be provided in order to accommodate transmission of the anchorage loads to the opposite side of the supporting concrete member. Provision of appropriate hanger reinforcement is assumed to prevent any negative influence of the anchorage on the shear capacity of the concrete member. Given the relatively large allowable spacing between anchor and hanger reinforcement, hanger reinforcement as discussed here is not intended to increase the capacity of the anchorage.

The above conditions apply as well to slabs and beams made of prefabricated units and added cast-in-place concrete. In addition, anchor loads may be transmitted into the prefabricated concrete only if the safe transmission of the loads into the cast-in-place concrete can be shown. This condition may be assumed to be satisfied if the precast concrete is connected with the cast-in-place concrete by a shear reinforcement (e.g. stirrups) according to MC 90,[1] equation (6.10-1), with $\beta = 0.0$ (Fig. 34(a)). If this shear reinforcement between precast and cast-in-place concrete is not present, only the loads of suspended ceilings or similar constructions with a weight up to 1.0 kN/m$^2$ may be anchored in the precast concrete (Fig. 34(b)). Alternatively, the anchors should extend into the cast-in-place concrete and the anchorage depth in the precast concrete is then disregarded when calculating the anchor resistance (Fig. 34(c)).

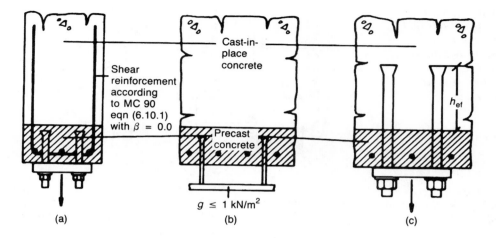

*Fig. 34. Fastenings in beams and slabs made of prefabricated concrete and added cast-in-place concrete*

*Comment*

The shear resistance of slabs and beams made of prefabricated concrete and added cast-in-place concrete depends on the amount of shear reinforcement crossing the joint area. If the shear reinforcement takes up all the shear forces, then the anchor loads may be transmitted into the precast concrete. However, if the shear reinforcement takes up only some of the shear forces or if precast concrete and cast-in-place concrete are not connected by a shear reinforcement, then the shear capacity of the structural member may be significantly reduced by anchor loads transmitted into the precast concrete, because they increase the tensile stresses in the joint area. In these applications, the anchor loads should be transmitted into the cast-in-place concrete only; therefore only the anchorage depth of the anchor in the cast-in-place concrete should be assumed to be effective. An exception is the fastening of suspended ceilings or similar constructions with a weight up to $1.0\,\mathrm{kN/m^2}$, because the tensile stresses in the joint area caused by this load are insignificant.

## 7.3. Resistance to splitting forces

In general, the splitting forces caused by anchors should be considered in the design of the concrete member. They may be neglected if one of the following conditions is met.

(*a*) The load transfer area is in the compression zone of the concrete member.

(*b*) Under the characteristic actions, the tension force $N_{Sk}$ of single anchors, or the resultant tension force $N_{Sk}^g$ of the tensioned anchors of an anchor group, is small (e.g. $\lesssim 10\,\mathrm{kN}$).

(*c*) Under the characteristic actions, the tension force $N_{Sk}$ of a single anchor, or the resultant tension force $N_{Sk}^g$ of the tensioned anchors of an anchor group, is smaller than or equal to $30\,\mathrm{kN}$. In addition, for anchorages in slabs and walls a concentrated reinforcement in both directions in the plane of the structure is present in the region of the anchorage. The area of the transverse reinforcement should be at least 60% of the longitudinal reinforcement required for the actions due to anchor loads.

*Comment*

Anchor splitting forces are induced in a concrete member by two actions:

(1) transfer of a concentrated load into the concrete member (compare Fig. 35(a) with Fig. 35(b));

(2) the wedging action of undercut anchors (a wedging action will occur also for headed anchors after the formation of a concrete wedge under the head at a high bearing pressure), by bond stresses caused by bonded

*Fig. 35. Splitting forces due to concentrated loads and simplified strut-and-tie models: (a) load applied at the concrete surface (compression); (b) load transmitted by anchor (tension)*

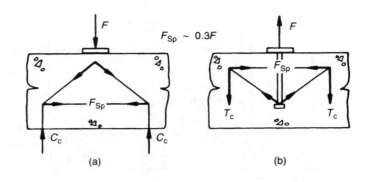

(a)  (b)

*Fig. 36. Increase of tension force in reinforcement due to anchor splitting forces*

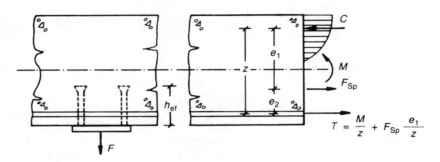

$$T = \frac{M}{z} + F_{Sp} \frac{e_1}{z}$$

anchors or by expanding torque-controlled or deformation-controlled anchors.

The splitting forces may be taken up by reinforcement or by compression forces if the load transfer area is located in the compression zone of the concrete member.

If anchors are located in the tension zone of a concrete member, in general the splitting forces will increase the tension force in the reinforcement (see Fig. 36). This should be taken into account in the design, if the conditions (*b*) or (*c*) given above are not observed. The ratio between the splitting force $F_{sp}$ and the anchor tension force $N$ should be given in the relevant approval certificate or should be evaluated in the prequalification procedure. If not, the following values should be considered as a first indication:

$F_{sp} = 0.5\,N$ for bonded and headed anchors
$F_{sp} = 1.0\,N$ for undercut anchors
$F_{sp} = 1.5\,N$ for torque-controlled expansion anchors
$F_{sp} = 2.0\,N_{Rd}$ for deformation-controlled expansion anchors

The limiting value of 30 kN in condition (*c*) is valid for a reinforcement ratio up to $\mu = A_s/(b \cdot h) \sim 0.5\%$. For a larger reinforcement ratio this value may be increased.

# 8. General

Part II (sections 8–13) is valid for fastenings with post-installed expansion and undercut anchors loaded by tension, shear, combined tension and shear forces as well as bending and torsion moments (see Figs 1–3).

To ensure suitability and durability of these anchors for use in structural concrete, prequalification testing should be performed. Anchors to be installed in a region where concrete cracking is likely to occur, or where no cracking is expected, should meet the requirements of appropriate specifications, e.g. as given by the *UEAtc Technical Guide on Anchors for Use in Cracked and Non-Cracked Concrete*,[9] the EOTA *Guideline for European Technical Approval of Anchors (Metal Anchors) for Use in Concrete*[10] or the ASTM *Standard Specification for Performance of Anchors in Cracked and Non-Cracked Concrete.*[11]

The anchors should be installed carefully according to the producer's written installation instructions. The position of the anchorages should comply with the corresponding drawings. Only positive tolerances are allowed for edge distance, spacing and anchorage depth. Furthermore, the installation requirements given in the approval document or evaluated in the prequalification procedure (e.g. according to Refs 9 to 11) should be complied with.

In general, the loading of the concrete member and the anchorage should be limited to predominantly static loading; for exceptions see section 11.

According to the safety concept of partial safety factors (see section 3.1, equation (1)), it should be shown that the design value of the actions do not exceed the design value of the resistance. Equation (1) should be observed for all loading directions (tension, shear, combined tension and shear) as well as for all failure modes (steel failure, pull-out failure and concrete failure).

The calculation of the load distribution to the anchors may always be performed according to the theory of elasticity (see section 4.2.1). In certain cases it may be permissible to calculate this distribution according to the theory of plasticity (see section 4.2.2).

In the following sections equations for calculating the characteristic resistance for both design approaches are given for all loading directions and all failure modes. Furthermore, requirements are given for the ultimate limit state of fatigue, the serviceability limit state, and to ensure durable anchorages.

The behaviour of anchorages can be improved by suitably dimensioned and detailed reinforcement crossing the failure surface. In general, the influence of this reinforcement on the strength of anchorages is neglected in Part II of the Design Guide, because usually the position of the reinforcement with respect to post-installed anchors is not known. However, requirements for the minimum reinforcement are given in the appropriate sections to ensure the assumed resistance.

The minimum values for edge distance, spacing, member thickness and reinforcement, as well as the edge distance and spacing for developing the characteristic tension resistance for concrete cone failure and splitting failure given in the relevant approval certificate or evaluated in the prequalification procedure (e.g. according to Refs 9 to 11), are valid.

Flowcharts for calculating the resistance for the elastic and plastic design approaches are given in Figs 37 and 38.

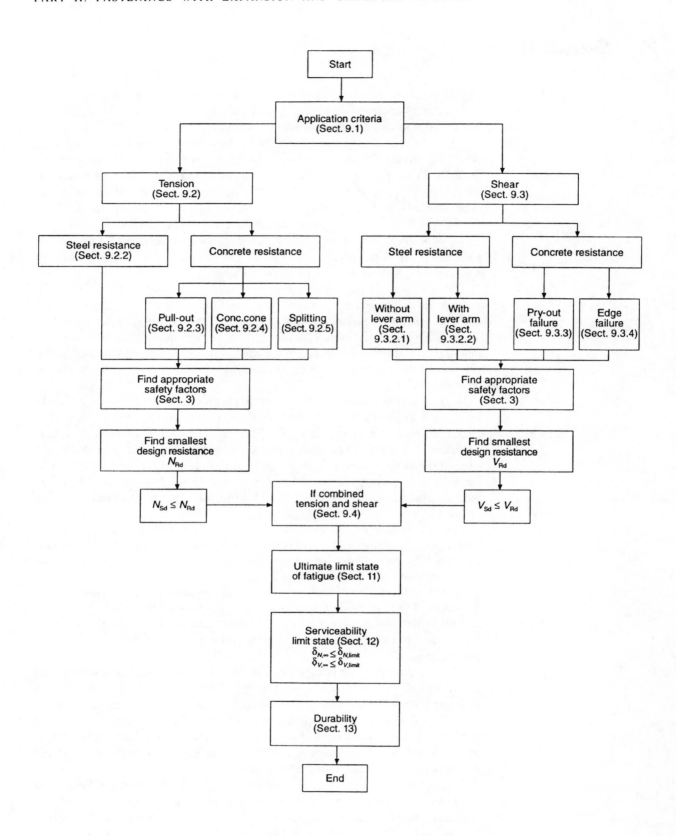

*Fig. 37. Flowchart B for the calculation of the resistance of post-installed expansion and undercut anchors (elastic design approach)*

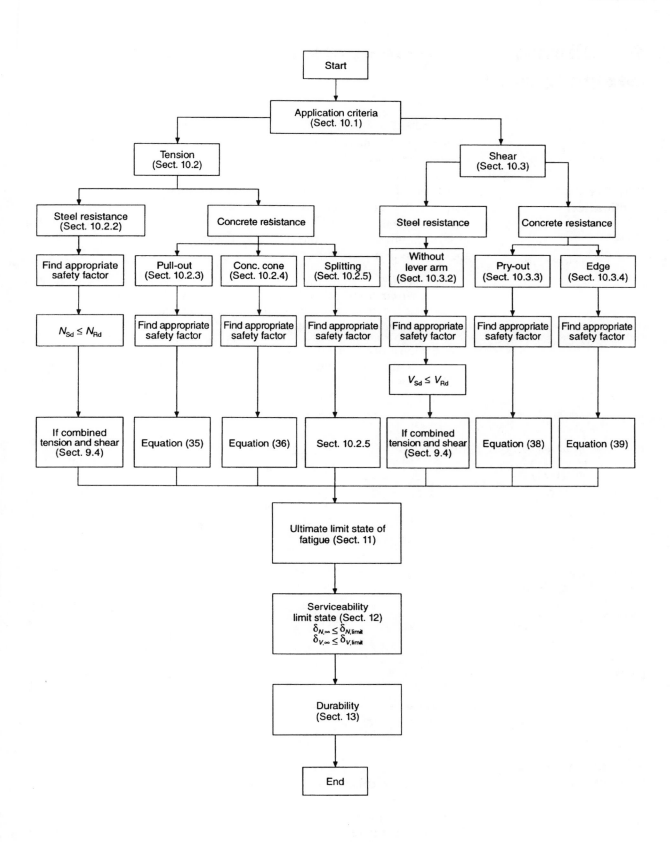

*Fig. 38. Flowchart C for the calculation of the resistance of post-installed expansion and undercut anchors (plastic design approach)*

# 9. Ultimate limit state of resistance — elastic design approach

In the elastic design approach the distribution of loads on the fixture to the anchors of an anchor group is performed according to the theory of elasticity (see section 4.2.1).

## 9.1. Field of application

Part II of this Design Guide covers single anchors and anchor groups with post-installed expansion and undercut anchors according to Fig. 39.

Fastenings may consist of one to six anchors. This document assumes that groups of three anchors are arranged linearly and groups of four or six anchors are in a rectangular pattern.

> *Comment*
> Fastener arrangements with more than six anchors and/or in a triangular or circular pattern are also allowed. However, the provisions of this Guide should be applied with engineering judgement.

In the case of shear loads acting on the fixture it may occur that only a limited number of anchors take up shear load (see Fig. 40 and section 4.2.1.3, subsections $(a)(2)$ and $(a)(3)$). In general, a small edge distance in the sense of section 4.2.1.3, subsection $(a)(2)(i)$, should be assumed if the edge distance in any direction is $c < 60d$.

*Fig. 39. Typical anchorages which are covered by Part II of this Design Guide*

*Fig. 40. Typical anchorages situated close to an edge $(c < 60d)$ where, in case of concrete edge failure, only some of the anchors take up shear loads and contribute to the shear resistance of the group*

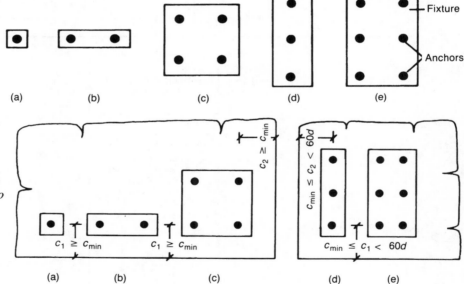

## 9.2. Resistance to tension load

### 9.2.1. Required verifications
The required verifications are summarized in Table 3.

### 9.2.2. Steel failure
The characteristic resistance $N_{Rk,s}$ of an anchor in the case of steel failure is obtained from equation (20)

$$N_{Rk,s} = A_s \cdot f_{yk} \tag{20}$$

with

$A_s$ = minimum cross-section along the stressed anchor length

*Table 3. Required verifications for tension loading (elastic design approach)*

|  | Single anchor | Anchor group |
|---|---|---|
| Steel failure | $N_{Sd} \leq N_{Rd,s} = N_{Rk,s}/\gamma_{Ms}$ | $N_{Sd}^h \leq N_{Rd,s} = N_{Rk,s}/\gamma_{Ms}$ |
| Pull-out failure | $N_{Sd} \leq N_{Rd,p} = N_{Rk,p}/\gamma_{Mp}$ | $N_{Sd}^h \leq N_{Rd,p} = N_{Rk,p}/\gamma_{Mp}$ |
| Concrete cone failure | $N_{Sd} \leq N_{Rd,c} = N_{Rk,c}/\gamma_{Mc}$ | $N_{Sd}^g \leq N_{Rd,c} = N_{Rk,c}/\gamma_{Mc}$ |
| Splitting failure | $N_{Sd} \leq N_{Rd,sp} = N_{Rk,sp}/\gamma_{M,sp}$ | $N_{Sd}^g \leq N_{Rd,sp} = N_{Rk,sp}/\gamma_{M,sp}$ |

*Comment*

If for certain anchors (e.g. bolt-type expansion anchors) the force at steel yielding cannot be measured, then

$$f_{yk} = 0.8 f_{uk} \tag{21}$$

should be inserted in equation (20).

### 9.2.3. Pull-out (pull-through) failure

The characteristic resistance $N_{Rk,p}$ of an anchor in the case of pull-out or pull-through failure should be evaluated from the results of appropriate tests in the prequalification procedure (e.g. according to Refs 9 to 11) or taken from the relevant approval certificate.

*Comment*

In the case of a pull-out failure the whole anchor is pulled out of the hole. This may occur with undercut anchors if the bearing area is too small. This failure mode should not be allowed with torque-controlled expansion anchors, because the failure load may depend significantly on the installation procedure. Pull-through failure is defined as pulling the cone through the sleeve. This failure mode is allowed for torque-controlled expansion anchors, because pulling the cone into the sleeve is the working principle of these anchor types and the failure load depends mainly on the quality of anchor manufacture.

### 9.2.4. Concrete cone failure

The characteristic resistance $N_{Rk,c}$ of an anchor or an anchor group in the case of concrete failure is given by equation (22):

$$N_{Rk,c} = N_{Rk,c}^0 \cdot \psi_{A,N} \cdot \psi_{s,N} \cdot \psi_{ec,N} \cdot \psi_{re,N} \cdot \psi_{ucr,N} \quad [N] \tag{22}$$

with

$N_{Rk,c}^0$ = characteristic resistance of a single anchor without edge and spacing effects, anchored in cracked concrete

$\psi_{A,N} = \dfrac{A_{c,N}}{A_{c,N}^0}$

= factor to take into account the geometric effects of spacing and edge distance

$\psi_{s,N}$ = factor to take into account the influence of edges of the concrete member on the distribution of stresses in the concrete

$\psi_{ec,N}$ = factor to take into account a group effect when different tension loads are acting on the individual anchors of a group

$\psi_{re,N}$ = shell spalling factor to take into account that the strength of anchors with a small anchorage depth ($h_{ef} < 100\,mm$) is reduced by reinforcement with a small spacing

$\psi_{ucr,N}$ = factor to take into account whether an anchorage is in cracked or non-cracked concrete

Fig. 41. Example of an
anchorage where the
compression force caused by
a bending moment acting on
the fixture may increase the
concrete cone capacity of the
tensioned anchor

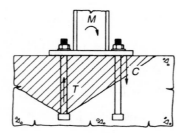

*Comment*
The characteristic resistance against the formation of a concrete cone may be
increased by a compression force acting on the concrete surface close to the
tensioned anchors, e.g. when a bending moment is acting on the fixture and the
anchor spacing is $s \stackrel{\sim}{<} 1.5h_{ef}$ (see Fig. 41). This influence is neglected in
equation (22), because a general design model is not yet available.

The different factors of equation (22) are given below.

(*a*) The characteristic resistance of a single anchor without edge and
spacing effects, anchored in cracked concrete, is calculated as:

$$N_{Rk,c}^0 = k_1 \cdot f_{ck}^{0.5} \cdot h_{ef}^{1.5} \quad [N] \tag{22a}$$

$$k_1 = 7.5 \ [N^{0.5}/mm^{0.5}]$$

*Comment*
Different $k_1$-values ($k_1 \leq 9.0$) may be taken, if proved in the prequalification
tests. For undercut anchors with a bearing area fulfilling the requirements
given in Part III, section 15.1.2.3, the factor $k_1$ might be increased to 9.0 as for
headed anchors.

According to equation (22a) the concrete cone resistance increases with
$h_{ef}^{1.5}$. This agrees with test results and can be explained by fracture mechanics.

(*b*) The factor $\psi_{A,N} = A_{c,N}/A_{c,N}^0$ takes into account the geometric effects
of spacing and edge distance, where:

$A_{c,N}^0$ = area of concrete cone of an individual anchor with a large
spacing and edge distance at the concrete surface, idealizing
the concrete cone as a pyramid with a height equal to $h_{ef}$ and
base lengths equal to $s_{cr,N}$ (see Fig. 42)

$A_{c,N}$ = actual area of concrete cone of the anchorage at the concrete
surface. It is limited by overlapping concrete cones of
adjacent anchors ($s < s_{cr,N}$) as well as by edges of the

Fig. 42. Idealized concrete
cone and area $A_{c,N}^0$ of
concrete cone of an
individual anchor loaded in
tension

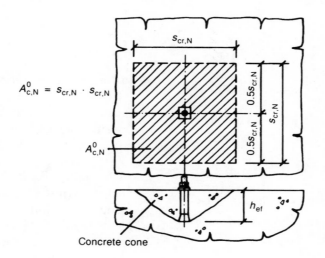

concrete member ($c < c_{cr,N}$). It may be deduced from the idealized failure cone (see Fig. 43). More examples for the calculation of $A_{c,N}$ are given in Fig. 44.

In general, the following values may be taken.

$$s_{cr,N} = 3.0h_{ef} \tag{22b1}$$

$$c_{cr,N} = 1.5h_{ef} \tag{22b2}$$

(*c*) The factor $\psi_{s,N}$ takes into account the influence of edges of the concrete member on the distribution of stresses in the concrete.

$$\psi_{s,N} = 0.7 + 0.3 \cdot \frac{c}{c_{cr,N}} \leq 1 \tag{22c}$$

For fastenings with several edge distances (e.g. a fastening in a corner or in a narrow member), the smallest edge distance, $c$, should be inserted in equation (22c).

*Comment*

Fastenings with a large edge distance show a rotationally symmetric distribution of stresses in the concrete. This distribution is disturbed if the anchor is located close to an edge. A similar disturbance of the stress distribution occurs with an anchor located in a crack.

*Fig. 43. Idealized concrete cone and area $A_{c,N}$: (a) anchor group ($s < s_{cr,N}$) far from edges; (b) single anchor at an edge ($c_1 < c_{cr,N}$)*

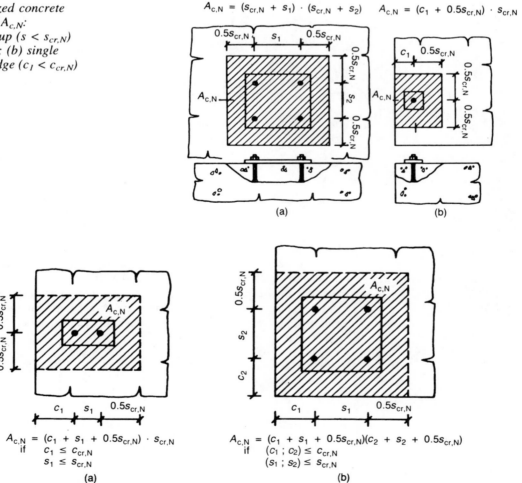

$A_{c,N} = (s_{cr,N} + s_1) \cdot (s_{cr,N} + s_2)$
$A_{c,N} = (c_1 + 0.5s_{cr,N}) \cdot s_{cr,N}$
0.5$s_{cr,N}$
$s_1$
0.5$s_{cr,N}$
$s_2$
$A_{c,N}$
$c_1$
(a)
(b)


$A_{c,N}$
0.5$s_{cr,N}$
$c_1$
$s_1$
$s_2$
$c_2$
$A_{c,N} = (c_1 + s_1 + 0.5s_{cr,N}) \cdot s_{cr,N}$
if $c_1 \leq c_{cr,N}$
$s_1 \leq s_{cr,N}$
(a)
$A_{c,N} = (c_1 + s_1 + 0.5s_{cr,N})(c_2 + s_2 + 0.5s_{cr,N})$
if $(c_1 ; c_2) \leq c_{cr,N}$
$(s_1 ; s_2) \leq s_{cr,N}$
(b)


*Fig. 44. Examples of actual areas $A_{c,N}$ of the idealized concrete cones for different anchor arrangements in the case of tension load: (a) group of two anchors at the edge of a concrete member; (b) group of four anchors at the corner of a concrete member*

(d) The factor $\psi_{ec,N}$ takes into account a group effect when different tension loads are acting on the individual anchors of a group.

$$\psi_{ec,N} = \frac{1}{1 + 2e_N/s_{cr,N}} \leq 1 \qquad (22d)$$

with

$e_N$ = eccentricity of the resulting tensile force acting on the tensioned anchors with respect to the centre of gravity of the tensioned anchors (see section 4.2.1.2). Where there is an eccentricity in two directions (see Fig. 19(c)), $\psi_{ec,N}$ should be determined separately for each direction according to equation (22d) and the product of both factors should be inserted in equation (22).

*Comment*
For the example shown in Fig. 19(c), $\psi_{ec,N}$ to be inserted in equation (22) is

$$\psi_{ec,N} = \frac{1}{1 + 2e_{N,1}/s_{cr,N}} \cdot \frac{1}{1 + 2e_{N,2}/s_{cr,N}}$$

As a simplification, a factor $\psi_{ec,N} = 1.0$ may be assumed, if for groups the most stressed anchor is verified according to $N_{Sd}^h \leq N_{Rk,c}^h/\gamma_{Mc}$ and the resistance of this anchor is taken as

$$N_{Rk,c}^h = N_{Rk,c}/n \qquad (22e)$$

with $N_{Rk,c}$ according to equation (22) with $\psi_{ec,N} = 1.0$, and
$n$ = number of tensioned anchors

(e) The shell spalling factor $\psi_{re,N}$ takes into account that the strength of anchors with a small embedment depth is reduced by reinforcement with a small bar spacing $s$.

$$\psi_{re,N} = 0.5 + \frac{h_{ef}\,[mm]}{200} \leq 1 \text{ for } s < 150 \text{ mm (for any diameter)}$$
$$\text{or } s < 100 \text{ mm (for } d_s \leq 10 \text{ mm)} \quad (22f)$$

$$\psi_{re,N} = 1.0 \qquad\qquad \text{for } s \geq 150 \text{ mm (for any diameter)}$$
$$\text{or } s \geq 100 \text{ mm (for } d_s \leq 10 \text{ mm)} \quad (22g)$$

*Comment*
For fastenings in the vicinity of reinforcement, the tensile stresses in concrete induced by the fastening and by the bond action of reinforcement overlap. This overlapping is especially pronounced for small bar spacings. Furthermore, with closely spaced reinforcement, the concrete strength in the region of the reinforcement may be lower than in the core of the member. Both effects will reduce the strength of a fastening.

(f) The factor $\psi_{ucr,N}$ takes into account whether the anchorage is in cracked or non-cracked concrete.

$\psi_{ucr,N} = 1.0$ for anchorages in cracked concrete $\qquad (22h)$
$\psi_{ucr,N} = 1.4$ for anchorages in non-cracked concrete $\qquad (22i)$

The factor $\psi_{ucr,N} = 1.4$ should be used only if in each individual case it is shown according to section 5, that the concrete in which the anchor is placed is non-cracked.

*Comment*
Certain types of torque-controlled expansion anchors and deformation-controlled expansion anchors according to Part I, Fig. 5, may not be suitable for transferring tension loads into cracked concrete. Therefore these anchors may only be used in concrete which is non-cracked in the proximity of the anchor.

(*g*) Special cases: for anchorages with three or more edges with an edge distance $c_{max} < c_{cr,N}$ ($c_{max}$ = largest edge distance; for examples see Fig. 45) the calculation according to equation (22) leads to results which are on the safe side.

More accurate results are obtained if in equation (22a) the embedment depth $h_{ef}$ is replaced by the value

$$h'_{ef} = \frac{c_{max}}{c_{cr,N}} \cdot h_{ef} \qquad (22j)$$

and if in equations (22c) and (22d) as well as for the calculation of $A^0_{c,N}$ and $A_{c,N}$ (compare Figs 42 to 44) the values

$$s'_{cr,N} = 2c_{max} \qquad (22k)$$

$$c'_{cr,N} = c_{max} \qquad (22l)$$

are inserted for $s_{cr,N}$ and $c_{cr,N}$ respectively.

### 9.2.5. Splitting failure

*Comment*
At the time of writing this document, the characteristic splitting resistance cannot be predicted very accurately. However, it is believed that the following provisions are conservative.

If the edge distance of an anchor is smaller than the value of $c_{cr,sp}$ ($c_{cr,sp}$: see section 9.2.5.2), then a longitudinal reinforcement should be provided along the edge of the member to prevent splitting cracks attaining excessive width.

*9.2.5.1. Splitting failure due to anchor installation.* Splitting failure is avoided during anchor installation by compliance with certain minimum values for edge distance, spacing, member thickness and reinforcement. These values are given in the relevant approval certificate or should be evaluated from the results of appropriate tests in the prequalification procedure (e.g. according to Refs 9 to 11). The following values may be considered as a first approximation.

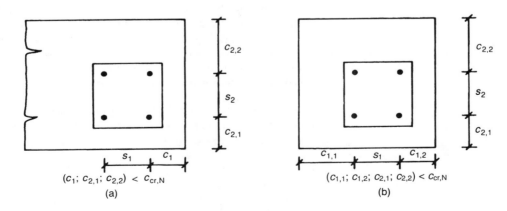

*Fig. 45. Examples of anchorages in concrete members where $h'_{ef}$, $s'_{cr,N}$ and $c'_{cr,N}$, may be used: (a) anchorage with three edges; (b) anchorage with four edges*

$$c_{min} = 1.0h_{ef} \quad \text{for undercut anchors} \tag{23a}$$

$$c_{min} = 2.0h_{ef} \quad \text{for torque-controlled expansion anchors with} \\ \text{one cone} \tag{23b}$$

$$c_{min} = 3.0h_{ef} \quad \text{for torque-controlled expansion anchors with} \\ \text{two cones and deformation-controlled expansion} \\ \text{anchors} \tag{23c}$$

$$s_{min} = 1.0h_{ef} \quad \text{for undercut and torque-controlled expansion} \\ \text{anchors} \tag{24a}$$

$$s_{min} = 3.0h_{ef} \quad \text{for deformation-controlled expansion anchors} \tag{24b}$$

$$h_{min} = 2.0h_{ef} \quad \text{for all anchor types} \tag{25}$$

### 9.2.5.2. Splitting failure due to anchor loading

(a) It may be assumed that splitting failure will not occur if the edge distance in all directions is $c \geq c_{cr,sp}$ (single anchors) or $c \geq 1.5c_{cr,sp}$ (anchor groups) and the member depth is $h \geq 2h_{ef}$.

*Comment*

For test purposes, the characteristic edge distance $c_{cr,sp}$ is evaluated for single anchors. This ensures that single anchors with $c \geq c_{cr,sp}$ will reach the concrete cone failure load according to equation (22a). The edge distance for anchor groups should be larger than $c_{cr,sp}$ to preclude a splitting failure because of the higher splitting forces generated by the group.

Values for $c_{cr,sp}$ and $s_{cr,sp}$ should be given in the relevant approval certificate or be evaluated from the results of appropriate tests during the prequalification procedure (e.g. according to Refs 9 to 11). The following values, which are valid for a member depth $h = 2h_{ef}$, may be considered as a first approximation.

$$c_{cr,sp} = 0.5\, s_{cr,sp} \\ = 2h_{ef} \text{ for undercut anchors} \tag{26a}$$

$$c_{cr,sp} = 3h_{ef} \text{ for expansion anchors} \tag{26b}$$

(b) With anchors suitable for use in cracked concrete, the calculation of the characteristic splitting resistance may be omitted if the following two conditions are fulfilled.

(1) Reinforcement is present which limits the crack width to a normal value of about 0.3 mm, taking into account the splitting forces according to section 7.3.

(2) The characteristic resistance for concrete cone failure $N_{Rk,c}$, according to equation (22) and for pull-out failure (see section 9.2.3), is calculated for cracked concrete independently of the position of the anchorage in cracked or non-cracked concrete.

*Comment*

The anchor splitting forces may cause splitting cracks in the concrete. However, if the concrete member is reinforced and the crack width due to quasi-permanent actions including the splitting forces induced by the anchors is limited to $w_k \sim 0.3$ mm, then the concrete cone resistance and the pull-out resistance valid for anchors in cracked concrete will be reached. Of course, the anchor must be suitable for use in cracked concrete.

(c) If either of the above conditions (a) and (b) is not fulfilled, then the characteristic resistance of a single anchor or an anchor group in the case of splitting failure should be calculated according to equation (27):

$$N_{Rk,sp} = N_{Rk,c}^0 \cdot \psi_{A,N} \cdot \psi_{s,N} \cdot \psi_{ec,N} \cdot \psi_{re,N} \cdot \psi_{ucr,N} \cdot \psi_{h,N} \quad [\text{N}] \tag{27}$$

with $N_{Rk,c}^0$, $\psi_{s,N}$, $\psi_{ec,N}$, $\psi_{re,N}$ and $\psi_{ucr,N}$ according to equations (22a) to (22i) and $\psi_{A,N} = A_{c,N}/A_{c,N}^0$ as defined in section 9.2.4, subsection (b); however, the values $c_{cr,N}$ and $s_{cr,N}$ should be replaced by $c_{cr,sp}$ and $s_{cr,sp}$ (the values $c_{cr,sp}$ and $s_{cr,sp}$ are defined in section 9.2.5.2(a)).

$\psi_{h,N}$ = factor to account for the influence of the actual member depth, $h$, on the splitting failure load

$$= \left(\frac{h}{2h_{ef}}\right)^{2/3} \leq 1.2 \tag{27a}$$

*Comment*

Equation (27) is an approximation, because the splitting failure load depends partly on parameters other than the concrete cone failure load. However, the approach is believed to be conservative.

If for certain anchors $c_{cr,N} \geq c_{cr,sp}$, then splitting failure will not occur and equation (27) may be neglected for all applications.

## 9.3. Resistance to shear load

*Comment*

For a consideration of friction forces in the design, see section 4.1.

### 9.3.1. Required verifications

The required verifications are summarized in Table 4.

*Table 4: Required verifications in the case of shear loading (elastic design approach)*

|  | Single anchor | Anchor group |
|---|---|---|
| Steel failure, shear load without lever arm | $V_{Sd} \leq V_{Rd,s} = V_{Rk,s}/\gamma_{Ms}$ | $V_{Sd}^{h} \leq V_{Rd,s} = V_{Rk,s}/\gamma_{Ms}$ |
| Steel failure, shear load with lever arm | $V_{Sd} \leq V_{Rd,sm} = V_{Rk,sm}/\gamma_{Ms}$ | $V_{Sd}^{h} \leq V_{Rd,sm} = V_{Rk,sm}/\gamma_{Ms}$ |
| Concrete pry-out failure | $V_{Sd} \leq V_{Rd,cp} = V_{Rk,cp}/\gamma_{Mc}$ | $V_{Sd}^{g} \leq V_{Rd,cp} = V_{Rk,cp}/\gamma_{Mc}$ |
| Concrete edge failure | $V_{Sd} \leq V_{Rd,c} = V_{Rk,c}/\gamma_{Mc}$ | $V_{Sd}^{g} \leq V_{Rd,c} = V_{Rk,c}/\gamma_{Mc}$ |

### 9.3.2. Steel failure

*9.3.2.1. Shear load without lever arm.* The characteristic resistance $V_{Rk,s}$ of an anchor in case of steel failure is obtained from equation (28):

$$V_{Rk,s} = k_2 \cdot A_s \cdot f_{yk} \quad \text{(N)} \tag{28}$$

with $k_2 = 0.6$ (—)

$A_s$ = stressed cross-section of anchor in the shear plane

*Comment*

For certain types of anchors with a reduced section along the length of the bolt, the characteristic resistance for steel failure $V_{RK,s}$ may be smaller than the value given by equation (28), because failure is caused by tension in the reduced section.

In a case where the sleeve of a sleeve-type anchor extends through the entire thickness of the fixture, the shear resistance $V_{Rk,s}$ of the anchor is increased beyond the capacity of the bolt, depending on the ductility and relative stiffnesses of the anchor sleeve and bolt. The degree to which the shear resistance is increased is highly dependent on the anchor design.

In both cases, the characteristic resistance should be taken from the relevant approval certificate or evaluated from the results of appropriate tests in the prequalification procedure (e.g. according to Refs 9 to 11).

In the case of anchor groups the shear resistance according to equation (28) should be multiplied by a factor of 0.8 if the anchor is made of steel with a rather low ductility, when the shear load is acting in the direction of a row of anchors and all anchors are assumed to take up shear loads (for examples see Figs 21(b) and 21(c)).

*Comment*
The factor 0.8 takes into account that the strength of a group of anchors made out of rather brittle steel is influenced by the limited shear deformability of the anchors when the shear load is acting in the direction of a row of anchors and all anchors are assumed to take up shear loads. This factor may be increased up to 1.0 for very ductile steel.

For other fastenings (see Fig. 23), the influence on the fastening behaviour of the diameter of the clearance hole with respect to the anchor diameter is taken into account in the determination of action effects (compare section 4.2.1.3(2)(ii)).

If the shear loads acting on the fastening undergo several reversals in direction, appropriate measures should be taken to avoid a fatigue failure of the anchor steel.

*Comment*
If an anchor is loaded by an alternating shear load $V \sim \pm V_{Rk,s}/(\gamma_Q \cdot \gamma_{Ms})$, a fatigue failure may occur after relatively few cycles ($< 100$). Therefore, if the direction of the shear force acting on the anchor varies frequently, appropriate measures should be taken to avoid a fatigue failure of the anchor steel; for example, the shear force should be transferred by friction between the fixture and the concrete (e.g. by assuring to a sufficiently high permanent prestressing force).

*9.3.2.2. Shear load with lever arm.* The characteristic resistance of an anchor, $V_{Rk,sm}$, is given by equation (29).

$$V_{Rk,sm} = \frac{\alpha_M \cdot M_{Rk,s}}{\ell} \leq V_{Rk,s} \quad [N] \tag{29}$$

where

$\alpha_M$ = a factor discussed in section 4.2.1.3, subsection (*c*)
$\ell$ = length of the lever arm according to equation (8)  [m]
$M_{Rk,s}$ = $M_{Rk,s}^0(1 - N_{Sd}/N_{Rd,s})$  [Nm]  (29a)
$M_{Rk,s}^0$ = characteristic bending resistance of an individual anchor
= $1.5 W_{el} \cdot f_{yk}$  [Nm]  (29b)
$N_{Rd,s}$ = $N_{Rk,s}/\gamma_{Ms}$
$N_{Rk,s}$ = characteristic resistance according to equation (20)
$\gamma_{Ms}$ = partial safety factor, according to section 3.2.3.2
$V_{Rk,s}$ = according to equation (28)

With anchor groups, $N_{Sd}$ should be replaced by $N_{Sd}^h$ in equation (29a).

*Comment*
For anchors with a significantly reduced section along the anchor length, the characteristic bending resistance should be calculated for the reduced section or evaluated by appropriate tests.

*9.3.3. Concrete pry-out failure*
Fastenings with short anchors may fail by prying out a concrete cone on the side opposite the load application. The corresponding characteristic resistance $V_{Rk,cp}$ is obtained from equation (30):

$$V_{Rk,cp} = k_3 \cdot N_{Rk,c} \tag{30}$$

with

$k_3$ = 1.0 for $h_{ef} < 60$ mm

= 2.0 for $h_{ef} \geq 60$ mm

$N_{Rk,c}$ = characteristic resistance according to section 9.2.4, determined for the anchors loaded in shear

*Comment*

The factor $k_3$ in equation (30) should be considered as a first approximation. More exact values for $k_3$ may be evaluated from the results of corresponding tests (e.g. according to Ref. 10).

### 9.3.4. Concrete edge failure

For fastenings shown in Fig. 39 with an edge distance in all directions $c \geq 60d$, it may be assumed that no concrete edge failure will occur.

The characteristic resistance of a single anchor or an anchor group in the case of concrete edge failure corresponds to:

$$V_{Rk,c} = V_{Rk,c}^0 \cdot \psi_{A,V} \cdot \psi_{h,V} \cdot \psi_{s,V} \cdot \psi_{ec,V} \cdot \psi_{\alpha,V} \cdot \psi_{ucr,V} \quad [N] \qquad (31)$$

where

$V_{Rk,c}^0$ = characteristic resistance of an anchor placed in cracked concrete and loaded perpendicular to the edge, without effects of spacing, further edges and member thickness.

$$\psi_{A,V} = \frac{A_{c,V}}{A_{c,V}^0}$$

= factor to take into account the geometric effects of spacing, member thickness and edge distances parallel to the direction of load

$\psi_{h,V}$ = factor to take into account that the resistance does not decrease linearly with the member thickness as assumed by the ratio $A_{c,V}/A_{c,V}^0$

$\psi_{s,V}$ = factor to take into account the influence of edges parallel to the loading direction on the distribution of stresses in the concrete

$\psi_{ec,V}$ = factor to take into account a group effect when different shear loads are acting on the individual anchors of a group

$\psi_{\alpha,V}$ = factor to take into account the angle between the shear load applied and the direction perpendicular to the free edge of the concrete member

$\psi_{ucr,V}$ = factor to take into account the position of the fastening in cracked or non-cracked concrete and the type of edge reinforcement used.

In the case of anchor groups close to an edge or corner, only the most unfavorable anchor or the two anchors placed most unfavorably near to an edge or corner of the concrete member should be taken into account for the determination of $V_{Rk,c}$ (see the dark anchors in Figs 46(a) and 47) (compare section 4.2.1.3, subsection (a)(2)(i)). Only in the case of slotted holes, the anchor furthest from the edge is decisive for the calculation of $V_{Rk,c}$ (for an example, see Fig. 46(b)).

For fastenings placed at a corner, the characteristic resistance should be checked for both edges; the smallest value is decisive (for an example, see Fig. 47).

*Comment*

Care should be exercised in applying the correct angle of load direction, edge distance and spacings for the calculation of the characteristic resistance

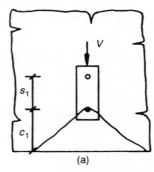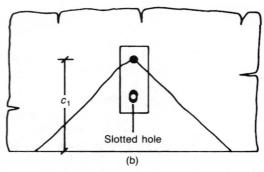

(a)　　　　　　　　　　　　　　(b)

Fig. 46. Example of a group of anchors near an edge under shear loading: (a) anchorage without slotted hole; (b) anchorage with slotted hole

Fig. 47. Example of a group of anchors at a corner under shear loading (resistance should be checked for both edges)

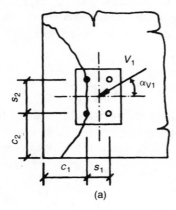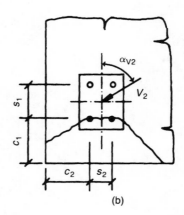

(a)　　　　　　　　　　　　　　(b)

according to equation (31). Because $c_1$ is always defined as the edge distance in the direction perpendicular to the edge considered for the calculation of the concrete resistance, the indices of the spacing and edge distance in Fig. 47(b) have been changed.

The various factors in equation (31) are explained below.

(a) The characteristic resistance of an anchor with large values for spacing, distances of edges parallel to the loading direction and member thickness, placed in cracked concrete and loaded perpendicular to the edge, corresponds to:

$$V^0_{Rk,c} = k_4 \cdot d^{0.5}_{nom} \cdot (\ell_f/d_{nom})^{0.2} \cdot f^{0.5}_{ck} \cdot c^{1.5}_1 \quad [N] \tag{31a}$$

$$k_4 = 0.5 \quad [N^{0.5}/mm]$$

For $d_{nom}$ only values up to 30 mm and for $\ell_f/d_{nom}$ only values up to 8 mm should be inserted in equation (31a).

Comment

According to equation (31a) the concrete resistance increases with $c_1^{1.5}$. This agrees with test results and can be explained by fracture mechanics.

The inclusion of $d_{nom}$ and $\ell_f$ in equation (31a) takes into account the influence of the anchor stiffness on the concrete resistance.

(b) The geometric effects of spacing, distances of edges parallel to the direction of load and thickness of the concrete member on the characteristic resistance are taken into account by the factor

$$\psi_{A,V} = A_{c,V}/A^0_{c,V}$$

where

*Fig. 48. Idealized concrete cone and area $A^0_{c,V}$ of concrete cone of a single anchor loaded in shear*

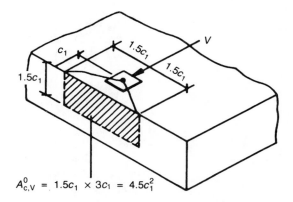

$$A^0_{c,V} = 1.5c_1 \times 3c_1 = 4.5c_1^2$$

$A^0_{c,V}$ = area of concrete break-out body of a single anchor at the lateral concrete surface not affected by edges parallel to the assumed loading direction, member thickness or adjacent anchors, idealizing the shape of the fracture body as a half-pyramid with a height equal to $c_1$ and base lengths of $1.5c_1$ and $3c_1$ (Fig. 48)

$\qquad = 4.5c_1^2$ $\hfill$ (31b)

$A_{c,V}$ = actual area of concrete cone of the fastening at the lateral concrete surface. It is limited by overlapping concrete fracture bodies of adjacent anchors ($s < 3c_1$), by edges parallel to the assumed loading direction ($c_2 < 1.5c_1$), and by member thickness ($h < 1.5c_1$). It may be deduced from the idealized half-pyramid. Examples for the calculation of $A_{c,V}$ are given in Fig. 49.

For the calculation of $A^0_{c,V}$ and $A_{c,V}$ it is assumed that the shear loads are applied perpendicular to the edge of the concrete member.

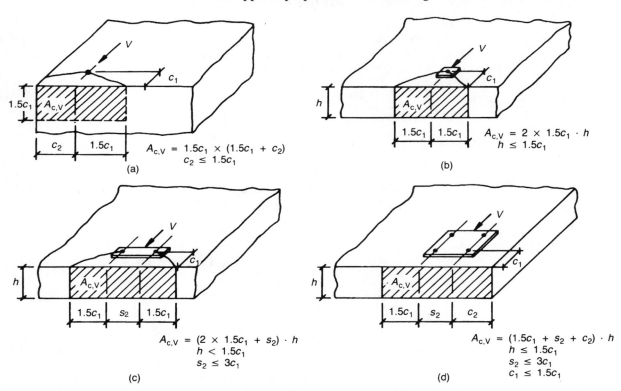

*Fig. 49. Examples of actual areas $A_{c,V}$ of the idealized half-pyramids for different anchor arrangements under shear load: (a) single anchor at a corner; (b) single anchor in a thin concrete member; (c) group of anchors in a thin concrete member; (d) group of anchors at a corner in a thin concrete member*

(c) The factor $\psi_{h,V}$ takes into account the fact that the resistance does not decrease linearly with the member thickness as assumed by the ratio $A_{c,V}/A^0_{c,V}$.

$$\psi_{h,V} = \left(\frac{1.5c_1}{h}\right)^{1/3} \geq 1 \tag{31c}$$

*Comment*
If the member thickness is $h < 1.5c_1$, the ratio $A_{c,V}/A^0_{c,V}$ gives a linear reduction of the anchor resistance with decreasing member depth. According to tests, the reduction of the anchor resistance is less pronounced. This is taken into account by the factor $\psi_{h,V}$.

(d) The factor $\psi_{s,V}$ takes into account the influence of edges of the concrete member parallel to the loading direction on the distribution of stresses in the concrete.

$$\psi_{s,V} = 0.7 + 0.3 \cdot \frac{c_2}{1.5c_1} \leq 1 \tag{31d}$$

For fastenings with two edges parallel to the direction of load (e.g. in a narrow concrete member) the smaller edge distance should be inserted in equation (31d).

(e) The factor $\psi_{ec,V}$ takes into account a group effect when different shear loads are acting on the individual anchors of a group.

$$\psi_{ec,V} = \frac{1}{1 + 2e_V/(3c_1)} \leq 1 \tag{31e}$$

where
  $e_V$ = eccentricity of the resulting shear load acting on the anchors relative to the centre of gravity of the anchors loaded in shear (see section 4.2.1.3, subsection (a) and Fig. 25)

*Comment*
For reasons of simplicity the eccentricity factor may be taken as $\psi_{ec,V} = 1.0$ if the most stressed anchor is verified according to $V^h_{Sd} \leq V^h_{Rk,c}/\gamma_{Mc}$ and the characteristic resistance of this anchor is taken as

$$V^h_{Rk,c} = V_{Rk,c}/n \tag{31f}$$

with $V_{Rk,c}$ according to equation (31) with $\psi_{ec,V} = 1.0$ and
$n$ = number of anchors loaded in shear

(f) The factor $\psi_{\alpha,V}$ takes into account the angle $\alpha_V$ between the load applied, $V_{Sd}$, and the direction perpendicular to the edge under consideration for the calculation of the concrete resistance of the concrete member (see Fig. 50).

$$\begin{aligned}
\psi_{\alpha,V} &= 1.0 & \text{for } 0° \leq \alpha_V \leq 55° \\
\psi_{\alpha,V} &= \frac{1}{\cos\alpha_V + 0.5\sin\alpha_V} & \text{for } 55° < \alpha_V \leq 90° \\
\psi_{\alpha,V} &= 2.0 & \text{for } 90° < \alpha_V \leq 180°
\end{aligned} \tag{31g}$$

*Comment*
For applications shown in Fig. 50(b), the above approach is a simplification which is conservative. It gives a transition of the anchor resistance for all values of $\alpha_V$ (see Fig. 51).

For the applications shown in Fig. 50(b) the above approach is taken as a conservative simplification due to lack of data. If sufficient data did exist, it is anticipated that the resistance of the anchors in this case will be determined by an appropriate concrete pry-out model.

*Fig. 50. Definition of angle $\alpha_V$*

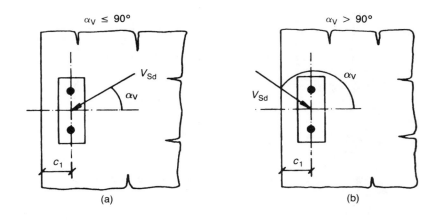

*Fig. 51. Factor $\psi_{\alpha,V}$*

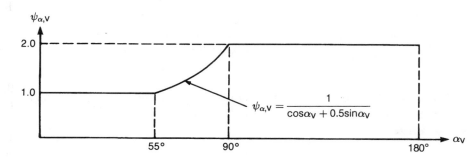

$$\psi_{\alpha,V} = \frac{1}{\cos\alpha_V + 0.5\sin\alpha_V}$$

(g) The factor $\psi_{ucr,V}$ takes into account the effect of the position of the fastening in cracked or non-cracked concrete and the type of edge reinforcement used.

$\psi_{ucr,V} = 1.0$    for fastenings in cracked concrete without edge reinforcement or stirrups

$\psi_{ucr,V} = 1.2$    for fastenings in cracked concrete with straight edge reinforcement ($d_s \geq 12$ mm) (see Fig. 52(a))

$\psi_{ucr,V} = 1.4$    for fastenings in cracked concrete with edge reinforcement and closely spaced stirrups ($\leq 100$ mm) (see Fig. 52(b)) or welded wire mesh with $d_s \geq 8$ mm and $s \leq 100$ mm (see Fig. 52(c)), and fastenings in non-cracked concrete (for the definition of non-cracked concrete see section 5)

(h) Special cases: for fastenings in a narrow, thin member with $c_{2,\max} < 1.5c_1$ ($c_{2,\max}$ = larger of the two distances to the edges parallel to the direction of loading) and $h < 1.5c_1$ (for an example,

*Fig. 52. Fastening at an edge loaded in shear: (a) with edge reinforcement; (b) with edge reinforcement and closely spaced stirrups; (c) with welded wire mesh*

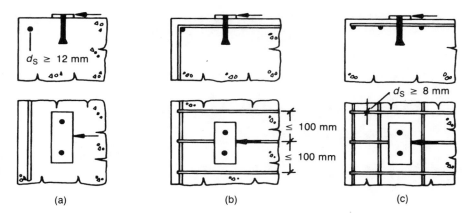

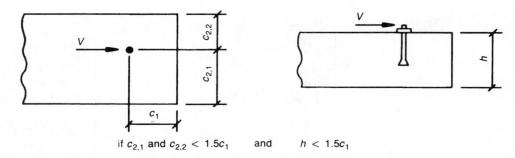

if $c_{2,1}$ and $c_{2,2} < 1.5c_1$     and     $h < 1.5c_1$

*Fig. 53. Example of a fastening in a narrow, thin member where $c_1'$ may be used instead of $c_1$*

see Fig. 53) the calculation according to equation (31) leads to results which are on the safe side.

More accurate results are obtained if in equations (31a), (31c) to (31e) and for the calculation of $A_{c,V}^0$ and $A_{c,V}$ (compare Figs 48 and 49) the edge distance $c_1$ is replaced by $c_1'$, this being the greater of the two values $c_{2,max}/1.5$ and $h/1.5$.

### 9.4 Resistance to combined tension and shear load

For combined tension and shear loads the following conditions (compare Fig. 54) should be satisfied:

$$N_{Sd}/N_{Rd} \leq 1 \qquad (32a)$$

$$V_{Sd}/V_{Rd} \leq 1 \qquad (32b)$$

$$(N_{Sd}/N_{Rd}) + (V_{Sd}/V_{Rd}) \leq 1.2 \qquad (32c)$$

For the ratios $N_{Sd}/N_{Rd}$ and $V_{Sd}/V_{Rd}$ the largest value for the different failure modes (compare Tables 3 and 4) should be inserted in equation (32).

*Comment*
In general, equation (32) yields conservative results for steel failure. More accurate results are obtained by equation (33).

$$\left(\frac{N_{Sd}}{N_{Rd}}\right)^\alpha + \left(\frac{V_{Sd}}{V_{Rd}}\right)^\alpha \leq 1 \qquad (33)$$

with $N_{Sd}/N_{Rd}$ and $V_{Sd}/V_{Rd}$ as given by equation (32), $\alpha = 2.0$ if $N_{Rd}$ and $V_{Rd}$ are governed by steel failure, and $\alpha = 1.5$ for all other failure modes; $\alpha = 1.0$ may be taken as a simplification.

*Fig. 54. Interaction diagram for combined tension and shear loads*

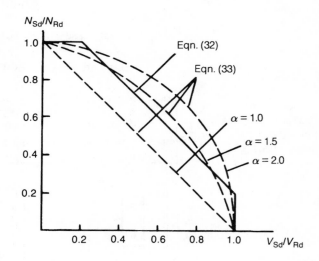

# 10. Ultimate limit state of resistance — plastic design approach

In the plastic design approach the distribution of loads on the fixture to the anchors of a group is performed according to the theory of plasticity (see section 4.2.2).

In general, the complete anchorage is checked according to equation (1). Therefore the required verifications are written for the group.

**10.1. Field of application**

The plastic design approach is allowed only if the conditions given in section 4.2.2.1, are satisfied.

**10.2. Resistance to tension load**

### 10.2.1. Required verifications
The required verifications are summarized in Table 5.

*Table 5. Required verifications for tension loading (plastic design approach)*

|  | Anchor group |
|---|---|
| Steel failure | $N_{Sd}^g \leq N_{Rk,s}^g / \gamma_{Ms}$ |
| Pull-out failure | Equation (35) |
| Concrete cone failure | Equation (36) |
| Splitting failure | See section 10.2.5 |

Only those anchors shall be assumed to transfer a tension force which satisfy equation (14) in section 4.2.2.2.

### 10.2.2. Steel failure
The characteristic resistance, $N_{Rk,s}$, of one anchor in the case of steel failure is obtained from section 9.2.2. The characteristic resistance of a group of tensioned anchors, $N_{Rk,s}^g$, may be taken as equal to the sum of the characteristic resistances of the anchors loaded in tension (equation (34)).

$$N_{Rk,s}^g = n \cdot N_{Rk,s} \tag{34}$$

with $N_{Rk,s}$ obtained according to section 9.2.2 and
$n$ = number of tensioned anchors

> *Comment*
> In equation (34) the same diameter and steel strength are assumed for all tensioned anchors of a group.

### 10.2.3. Pull-out or pull-through failure
For the characteristic resistance $N_{Rk,p}$ of one anchor in the case of pull-out or pull-through failure, see section 9.2.3. To satisfy equation (10) of section 4.2.2.1, the pull-out resistance of all tensioned anchors should meet equation (35):

$$N_{Rk,p}/\gamma_{Mp} \geq 1.25 \times \frac{N_{Rk,s}}{\gamma_{Ms}} \cdot \frac{f_{uk}}{f_{yk}} \tag{35}$$

with $N_{Rk,p}$ according to section 9.2.3, $N_{Rk,s}$ according to section 9.2.2, $\gamma_{Mp}$ according to section 3.2.3.1, and $\gamma_{Ms}$ according to section 3.2.3.2.

*Comment*
Equation (35) ensures that steel failure will occur before the pull-out resistance is reached.

### 10.2.4. Concrete cone failure
Section 9.2.4 applies without modification.

*Comment*
If in the design a constant tension force is assumed for all tensioned anchors, then the eccentricity factor is $\psi_{ec,N} = 1.0$.

To satisfy equation (10) of section 4.2.2.1, the anchorage depth should be large enough for equation (36) to be met:

$$\frac{N_{Rk,c}}{\gamma_{Mc}} \geq 1.25 \times \frac{N_{Rk,s}^g}{\gamma_{Ms}} \cdot \frac{f_{uk}}{f_{yk}} \tag{36}$$

with $N_{Rk,c}$ according to equation (22) and $N_{Rk,s}^g$ according to equation (34). For $\gamma_{Mc}$ and $\gamma_{Ms}$ see sections 3.2.3.1 and 3.2.3.2, respectively.

*Comment*
In equation (36) the same diameter, steel strength and anchorage depths are assumed for all anchors of a group.

### 10.2.5. Splitting failure
A splitting failure is avoided by complying with equation (36), where $N_{Rk,c}$ is replaced by $N_{Rk,cp}$ according to equation (27). Splitting failure may also be avoided by a sufficiently large edge distance to ensure steel failure. With anchors suitable for use in cracked concrete the verification of the splitting resistance may be omitted if the conditions in section 9.2.5.2, subsection (b) are met.

## 10.3. Resistance to shear load

### 10.3.1. Required verifications
The required verifications are summarized in Table 6.

*Table 6. Required verifications for shear loading (plastic design approach)*

| | Anchor groups |
| --- | --- |
| Steel failure, shear load without lever arm | $V_{Sd}^g \leq V_{Rk,s}^g / \gamma_{Ms}$ |
| Concrete pry-out failure | Equation (38) |
| Concrete edge failure | Equation (39) |

### 10.3.2. Steel failure
The characteristic resistance $V_{Rk,s}$ of one anchor is obtained from section 9.3.2.1. The characteristic resistance of a group of sheared anchors $V_{Rk,s}^g$ may be taken as equal to the sum of the characteristic resistances of the anchors loaded in shear (equation (37)).

$$V_{Rk,s}^g = n \cdot V_{Rk,s} \tag{37}$$

with $V_{Rk,s}$ obtained according to section 9.3.2.1, and
$n$ = number of sheared anchors.

*Comment*
Because a plastic design approach is allowed only for ductile steel, the factor 0.8 (see section 9.3.2.1) may be increased up to 1.0. In equation (37) the same diameter and steel strength are assumed for all sheared anchors of the group.

### 10.3.3. Concrete pry-out failure

Section 9.3.3 applies without modification. To satisfy equation (10) of section 4.2.2.1, the following condition should be met:

$$\frac{V_{Rk,cp}}{\gamma_{Mc}} \geq 1.25 \times \frac{V_{Rk,s}^{g}}{\gamma_{Ms}} \cdot \frac{f_{uk}}{f_{yk}} \tag{38}$$

with $V_{Rk,cp}$ according to section 9.3.3. and $V_{Rk,s}^{g}$ according to equation (37). For $\gamma_{Mc}$ and $\gamma_{Ms}$ see sections 3.2.3.1 and 3.2.3.2, respectively.

*Comment*
Equation (38) is satisfied if all anchors are anchored with an anchorage depth so that equation (36) is met.

### 10.3.4. Concrete edge failure

Section 9.3.4 applies without modification.

*Comment*
If in the design a constant shear force is assumed for all sheared anchors, then the eccentricity factor is $\psi_{ec} = 1.0$.

To satisfy equation (10) of section 4.2.2.1, the following condition should be met:

$$\frac{V_{Rk,c}}{\gamma_{Mc}} \geq 1.25 \times \left( \frac{V_{Rk,s}^{g}}{\gamma_{Ms}} \cdot \frac{f_{uk}}{f_{yk}} + V_{Rd,f} \right) \tag{39}$$

with

$V_{Rk,c}$ = characteristic edge failure load according to equation (31) for the anchor(s) closest to the edge

The value of $V_{Rk,s}^{g}$ is obtained according to equation (37) and $V_{Rd,f}$ according to section 4.1, equation (7); for $\gamma_{Mc}$ and $\gamma_{Ms}$ see sections 3.2.3.1 and 3.2.3.2, respectively.

*Comment*
If in the design the friction resistance is neglected, then $V_{Rd,f}$ may be omitted in equation (39).

## 10.4. Resistance to combined tension and shear load

Section 9.4 applies without modification.

*Comment*
The interaction equations (32) or (33) should be applied for the most loaded anchor. Then $N_{Rd}$ and $V_{Rd}$ are the design steel resistance in tension and shear, respectively, of that anchor.
Equation (33) with $\alpha = 1.0$ may be used for simplicity.

# 11. Ultimate limit state of fatigue

Fatigue loading of the structural member serving as base material or of the anchorage may be allowed for certain anchors, if this is stated in the relevant approval certificate or if it has been shown in the prequalification procedure that fatigue loads can be taken up by the anchor. In both cases the corresponding conditions (e.g. a permanent prestressing force of sufficient magnitude) and the allowable load should be met in the design.

The characteristic fatigue bending resistance of anchors in a stand-off installation to fasten facade elements is $\Delta\sigma_{\mathrm{sk,fat}} = 130\,\mathrm{MPa}$.

*Comment*
Due to temperature variations, fastenings of facade elements experience alternating shear loads. Therefore, either the facade elements are anchored so that no significant shear forces due to the restraint of deformations imposed on the facade element will occur in the fastening, or, in a stand-off installation, the bending stresses $\Delta\sigma = \max\sigma - \min\sigma$, in the most stressed anchor, caused by temperature variations, should be limited to avoid a steel fatigue failure. The value given above for $\Delta\sigma_{\mathrm{sk,fat}}$ is valid for about $10^4$ cycles of temperature variations.

# 12. Serviceability limit state

For the required verification see section 3.3.

The characteristic displacement of the anchor under given tension and shear loads may be taken from the relevant approval certificate or from the results of prequalification tests (e.g. according to Refs 9 to 11). It may be assumed that the displacements are a linear function of the applied load. In the case of a combined tension and shear load, the displacements for the tension and shear components of the resultant load should be added vectorially.

*Comment*
Usually, the characteristic displacements given in the approval certificate are valid for short-time loading. They may increase because of sustained loads or cracks with varying width caused by variable loads on the concrete structure. The increase depends on the type of loading and the type of anchor and may reach a factor of 1.5–2 for tension loading and 1.2–1.5 for shear loading. Furthermore, the shear displacements may increase due to a gap between fixture and anchor if the diameter of the clearance hole is larger than the diameter of the anchor.

# 13. Durability

It may be assumed that no corrosion of steel parts will occur if the anchorages are protected against corrosion as set out below.

(a) For anchorages for use in structures subject to dry internal conditions, in general, no special corrosion protection is necessary for steel parts, because coatings provided for preventing corrosion during storage prior to use and to ensure proper functioning (e.g. a zinc coating with a minimum thickness of $5 \mu$m) are considered sufficient. In general, malleable cast-iron parts do not require any protection.

(b) For anchorages for use in structures subject to normal atmospheric exposure or exposure in permanently damp internal conditions, the metal parts should be made of an appropriate grade of stainless steel. The grade of stainless steel suitable for the various service environments (marine, industrial etc.) should be in accordance with existing rules. Grade A4 of ISO 3506 or equivalent may be used indoors or outdoors if no particularly aggressive conditions exist.[13]

(c) In particularly aggressive conditions such as permanent or alternating immersion in seawater or in the splash zone of seawater, the chloride atmosphere of indoor swimming pools or an atmosphere with extreme chemical pollution (e.g. in desulphurization plants or road tunnels where de-icing materials are used) special consideration should be given to corrosion resistance. Current experience indicates that the type of stainless steel (A4) mentioned above will, in general, not have sufficient corrosion resistance in those aggressive conditions.

(d) If an anchor involves the use of different metals, these should be electrolytically compatible with each other. In dry internal conditions, carbon steel is compatible with malleable cast iron.

(e) If an anchor is coated to ensure its proper functioning (e.g. a torque-controlled expansion anchor) the durability of the coating should be shown in the prequalification tests (e.g. according to Ref. 10) for the intended conditions of use.

(f) Anchors used in structures where the base material might freeze should be installed in concrete that is suitable for freeze–thaw exposure. Furthermore, the entry of water into the holes should be prevented by suitable measures, e.g. sealing of the holes.

# 14. General

Part III (sections 14–19) is valid for fastenings with cast-in-place headed anchors (Fig. 55) loaded by tension, shear, and combined tension and shear forces, as well as bending and torsion moments. The anchors may be welded to the fixture (Fig. 55(d)), they may be threaded into the fixture, they may reach through the fixture (Fig. 55(a)) or they may be connected to the fixture by screws (Fig. 55(e)). In the cases shown in Figs 55(a) and 55(e), generally, there will be a gap between anchor and fixture as with post-installed anchors. The anchors may or may not be prestressed. L-bolts or J-bolts are not covered.

To ensure suitability of these anchors in structural concrete, prequalification testing may be necessary (e.g. analogous to the tests specified in Refs 9 to 11). Suitability tests may be omitted, if the following conditions are met.

(1) The concrete pressure under the head does not exceed the value given in section 15.1.2.3 and section 18.
(2) The angle between the head and the anchor axis is $\geq 45°$. The thickness of the head is not less than $0.8d$ and the value $0.5\,(d_h - d)$ is not less than 4 mm.
(3) For anchors threaded into the fixture the thread length should not be smaller than the nominal anchor diameter.
(4) The loading of the concrete member is limited to predominantly static loading.

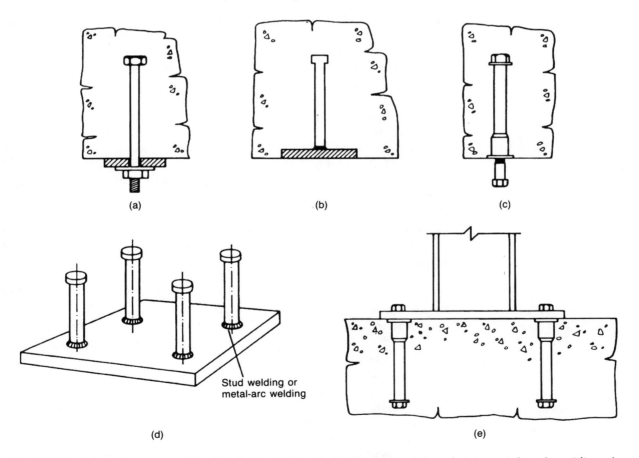

Fig. 55. Headed anchors covered by this Guide: (a) headed bolt; (b) headed stud; (c) special anchor; (d) anchor welded to the fixture; (e) fixture connected with the anchors by bolts

As a minimum, the manufacturer and the grade and type of steel should be marked on the anchor.

If anchors are welded to the fixture, this may be done by stud welding or metal arc welding according to the corresponding code of practice. In general, anchors made of stainless steel may not be welded to a fixture made of carbon steel. Failure of the weld should not occur. This should be checked by tests according to the corresponding code of practice.

> *Comment*
> The fixture is loaded perpendicular to its rolling direction. This should be taken into account when selecting the material and executing the welding.

The production of the anchors should be carried out under the manufacturer's quality assurance system with supervision by an independent body according to the relevant code of practice. This is also valid for the welding of the anchors and of the attachment to the fixture.

The anchorage should be carefully installed in the formwork according to the construction drawings. The correct position of the anchorage during casting should be ensured by appropriate methods and should be checked prior to casting in accordance with codes of practice for the control of reinforcement. Note that no negative tolerances are allowed for edge distance, spacing and embedment depth. Special care should be taken to ensure full compaction of the concrete in the region of the anchorage, and especially under the anchor heads. The attachment should be welded with care to the fixture at the position indicated in the drawings. Any extreme heating of the fixture that may cause damage in the adjacent concrete or high tension forces in the anchors should be avoided.

In general, the loading of the concrete member should be limited to predominantly static loading (no fatigue or seismic loading). However, fatigue loading of the concrete member, or seismic loading, may be allowed if appropriate tests have been performed to verify the behaviour of the anchor. The fastening may be subjected to predominantly static loadings or, in the case of anchors welded to or threaded into the fixture, to cycling loadings causing fatigue failure (see section 17). Fastenings with hanger reinforcement should be limited to predominantly static loadings.

According to the safety concept of partial safety factors, equation (1) of section 3.1 should be observed for all loading directions on the anchor (tension, shear, combined tension and shear) as well as for all failure modes (steel failure, pull-out failure and concrete failure).

The calculation of the load distribution to the anchors may always be performed according to the theory of elasticity (see section 4.2.1). In certain cases for fastenings without special reinforcement it may be permissible to calculate this distribution according to the theory of plasticity (see section 4.2.2).

The minimum values for edge distance, spacing, member thickness and reinforcement as well as the values for the edge distance $c_{cr,sp}$ and spacing $s_{cr,sp}$ in the relevant approval certificate or evaluated in the prequalification procedure (e.g. in analogy to Refs 9 to 11) are valid. If these values are not given in the approval certificate or have not been evaluated in the prequalification procedure, then the values proposed in this document may be considered as a first approximation.

For non-prestressed anchors fulfilling the above conditions (1) to (4), prequalification testing may be necessary to evaluate the values $c_{cr,sp} = 0.5s_{cr,sp}$, the characteristic displacements under given loads and the characteristic fatigue resistance. In addition, for prestressed anchors, prequalification testing is necessary for the evaluation of the minimum edge distance and minimum spacing for a given member depth (e.g. analogous to

Refs 9 to 11). Furthermore, prequalification testing may be necessary if the anchors are to be used in concrete members subjected to fatigue loading.

For non-prestressed anchors the minimum values for spacing, edge distance and member thickness given in Table 7 should be complied with.

*Table 7. Minimum values for spacing, edge distance and member thickness for non-prestressed headed anchors*

| | |
|---|---|
| Minimum spacing | $s_{min} = 5d \geq 50$ mm |
| Minimum edge distance | $c_{min} = 3d \geq 50$ mm |
| Minimum member thickness* | $h_{min} = h_{ef} + t_h + c_\phi$ |

\* $t_h$ = thickness of anchor head
$c_\phi$ = required concrete cover for reinforcement according to Ref. 1.

*Comment*
The minimum values for spacing, edge distance and member thickness should ensure that full compaction of the concrete in the region of the anchorage is possible.

In the following sections equations for calculating the characteristic resistance are given for anchorages without and with hanger reinforcement for all loading directions and all failure modes. Furthermore, requirements for the ultimate limit state of fatigue, the serviceability limit state, and to ensure durable anchorages, are given.

Flowcharts for calculating the resistance of anchorages with headed anchors according to the elastic and plastic design approaches are given in Figs 56–58.

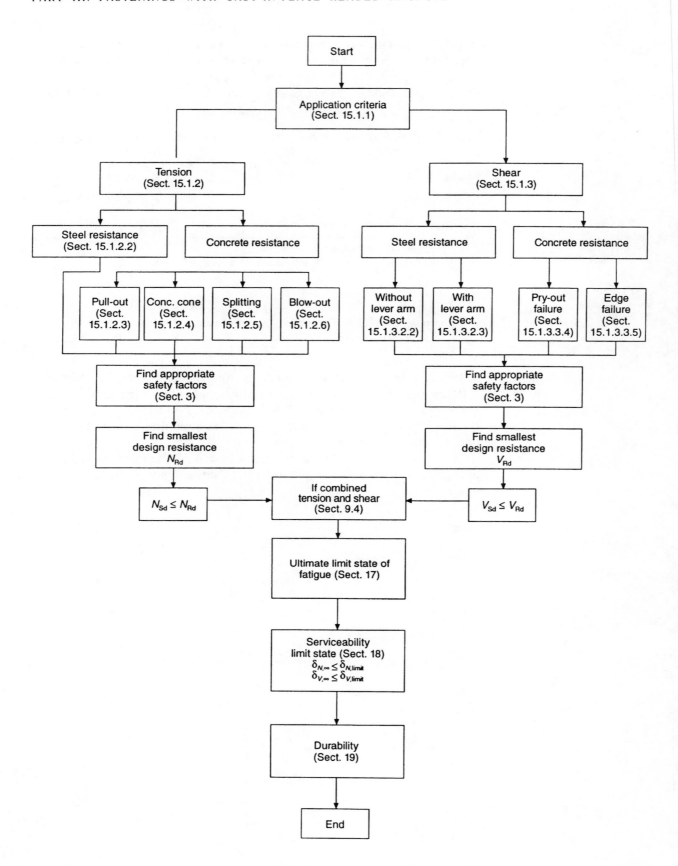

*Fig. 56. Flowchart B1 for the calculation of the characteristic resistances of anchorages with headed anchors without special reinforcement: elastic design approach*

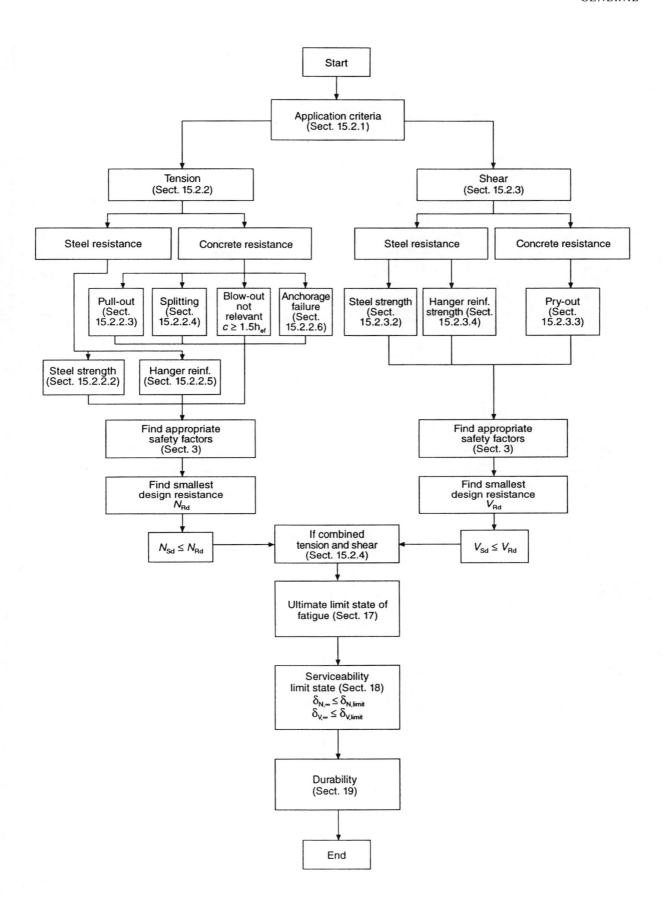

*Fig. 57. Flowchart B2 for the calculation of the characteristic resistances of anchorages with headed anchors with special reinforcement: elastic design approach*

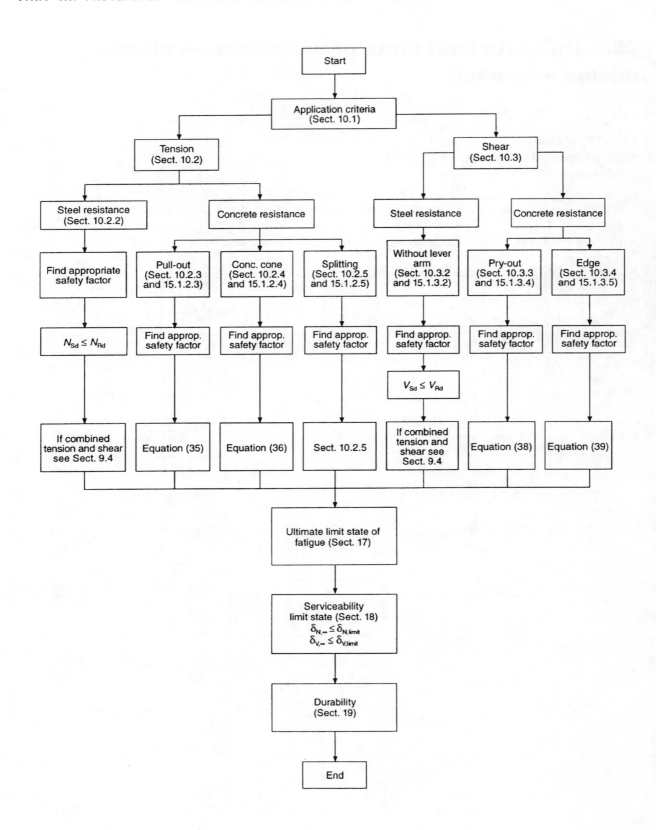

*Fig. 58. Flowchart C for the calculation of the characteristic resistances of anchorages with headed anchors without special reinforcement: plastic design approach*

# 15. Ultimate limit state of resistance — elastic design approach

## 15.1. Fastenings without special reinforcement

### 15.1.1. Field of application

Part III of this Design Guide covers single anchors and anchor groups with headed anchors welded to or threaded into the fixture according to Fig. 59. The anchorages may be located far from or close to edges. For anchorages with a clearance hole in the fixture, the field of application is given in Part II, section 9.1. For anchorages strengthened by special reinforcement, see also section 15.2.1.

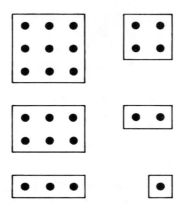

*Fig. 59. Typical anchorages with anchors welded to or threaded into the fixture which are covered by Part III of this Design Guide*

#### Comment
Fastener arrangements with more than nine anchors and/or in a triangular or circular pattern are also allowed for anchors welded to or threaded into the fixture. However, the provisions of this Guide should be applied with engineering judgement.

Welding together of multiple headed anchors is allowed; however, care should be exercised to align the anchors properly during assembly in order to avoid secondary eccentric moments. Consideration should also be given to the potential formation under service loads of a premature concrete failure cone originating from the anchor head closest to the concrete surface. To avoid this possibility, a soft material should be placed around the anchor head, as shown in Fig. 60.

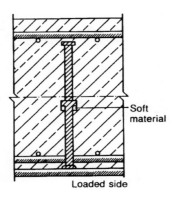

*Fig. 60. Example of a fastening with two anchors welded together*

#### Comment
The displacement to be accommodated by the soft material under the anchor head shown in Fig. 60 may be determined through appropriate consideration of elastic strain in the anchor shaft and corresponding head displacement under service loads. The soft material should be properly secured to the head to avoid displacement during casting.

### 15.1.2. Resistance to tension load

#### 15.1.2.1. Required verifications.
Section 9.2.1 applies.

#### 15.1.2.2. Steel failure.
Section 9.2.2 applies.

#### 15.1.2.3. Pull-out failure.
The characteristic pull-out resistance $N_{Rk,p}$ of an anchor is given by equation (40):

$$N_{Rk,p} = p_k A_h \quad [\text{N}] \tag{40}$$

with

$$p_k = 7.5 f_{ck} \text{ for cracked concrete} \qquad (40a)$$
$$p_k = 11 f_{ck} \text{ for non-cracked concrete} \qquad (40b)$$
$$A_h = \text{bearing area of the head}$$
$$= \pi(d^2_h - d^2)/4 \qquad (40c)$$

*Comment*
It may be necessary to reduce the pull-out capacity according to equation (40) to fulfil the requirements in the serviceability limit state (compare section 18 equation (52)).

*15.1.2.4. Concrete cone failure.* Section 9.2.4 applies, with the following modifications.

(a) The characteristic resistance, $N^0_{Rk,c}$, of a single anchor without edge and spacing effects situated in cracked concrete is calculated according to equation (22a) with $k_1 = 9.0$ [$N^{0.5}/mm^{0.5}$].

For anchorages with the fixture embedded in the concrete, the embedment depth may be calculated from the concrete surface if the idealized failure cone does not intersect with the fixture (Fig. 61(a)). If this condition is not fulfilled the embedment depth should be calculated from the surface of the fixture (Fig. 61(b)).

(b) If the distance of an anchor group perpendicular to the edge is $c < h_{ef}$, then a reinforcement in the form of stirrups ($d_s \geq 0.5d$, spacings $\leq 100$ mm) should be provided in the region of the anchorage (see Fig. 62).

*Comment*
According to the CC-Method, in the case of an anchor group perpendicular to the edge, the resistance of the anchors closest to and furthest away from the edge is averaged. This may be unconservative for fastenings with a rather small edge distance ($c < h_{ef}$). Therefore, in these applications, stirrups should be provided in the region of the fastening to increase the resistance.

*15.1.2.5. Splitting failure.*

*Comment*
At the time of writing this document, the characteristic splitting resistance cannot be predicted very accurately. However, it is believed that the following provisions are conservative.

*Fig. 61. Definition of the anchorage depth $h_{ef}$ for anchorages with a fixture embedded in the concrete*

*Fig. 62. Anchorage with $c/h_{ef} < 1$ with edge reinforcement in the form of stirrups*

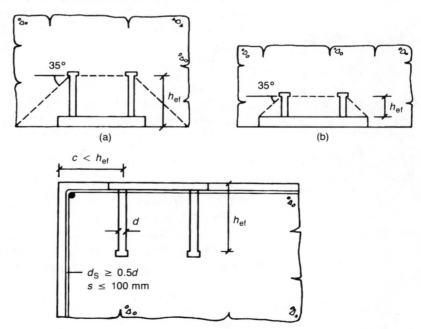

If the edge distance of an anchor is smaller than $c_{cr,sp}$ ($c_{cr,sp}$: see section 15.1.2.5.2) then a longitudinal reinforcement should be provided along the edge of the member.

*15.1.2.5.1. Splitting failure due to anchor installation.* Splitting failure is avoided during prestressing of headed anchors by complying with certain minimum values for edge distance, spacing, member thickness and reinforcement. These values are given in the relevant approval certificate or should be evaluated from the results of appropriate tests in the prequalification procedure (e.g. analogous to Refs 9 to 11). As a first approximation, the values valid for undercut anchors (see section 9.2.5.1) may be considered.

*15.1.2.5.2. Splitting failure due to anchor loading.* Section 9.2.5.2, subsections (*b*) and (*c*), apply.

> *Comment*
> Because groups with headed anchors may consist of a larger number of anchors at smaller spacings installed in a member with a smaller depth compared with expansion or undercut anchors, the simplified provision given in section 9.2.5.2, subsection (*a*), may be unconservative.
>
> Headed anchors complying with the provisions (1)–(4) in section 14 are suitable for use in cracked concrete. Therefore, in general, a splitting failure should be avoided by complying with the provisions of section 9.2.5.2, subsection (*b*). If in certain cases the characteristic splitting resistance is calculated according to equation (27), then the values $c_{cr,sp} = 0.5 s_{cr,sp} = 2 h_{ef}$ may be used.

*15.1.2.6. Local blow-out failure.* For anchorages with an edge distance $c > 0.5 h_{ef}$ in all directions, it may be assumed that a local blow-out failure will not occur.

The characteristic resistance of a single anchor or a row of anchors at the edge is given by equation (41):

$$N_{Rk,cb} = N^0_{Rk,cb} \cdot \psi_{A,Nb} \cdot \psi_{s,Nb} \cdot \psi_{ec,Nb} \cdot \psi_{ucr,Nb} \tag{41}$$

with

$N^0_{Rk,cb}$ = characteristic resistance of a single anchor at the edge unaffected by adjacent anchors, a corner or the member thickness, anchored in cracked concrete

$\psi_{A,Nb} = \dfrac{A_{c,Nb}}{A^0_{c,Nb}}$

= ratio to take into account the geometric effects of anchor spacing, edge distance in the second direction (corner) and member thickness

$\psi_{s,NB}$ = factor to take into account the influence of a corner on the distribution of stresses in the concrete

$\psi_{ec,Nb}$ = factor to take account of a group effect when different tension loads are acting on the individual anchors of a group

$\psi_{ucr,Nb}$ = factor to take account of the position of the anchorage in cracked or non-cracked concrete

> *Comment*
> For an anchor group rectangular in shape, the characteristic resistance of the group in the case of blow-out failure should be calculated according to equation (41) for the row of anchors closest to the edge. This approach is conservative.

The different factors of equation (41) are given below.

(a) The characteristic resistance of a single anchor at the edge unaffected by adjacent anchors, a corner or the member thickness, anchored in cracked concrete, is calculated as:

$$N_{Rk,cb}^0 = k_5 \cdot c_1 \cdot d \cdot f_{ck}^{0.5} \quad [N] \tag{41a}$$

$$k_5 = 8.0 \quad [N^{0.5}/mm]$$

*Comment*
Equation (41a) is valid for a ratio $d_h/d = 1.5$. For a ratio $d_h/d \neq 1.5$, the constant $k_5$ may be multiplied with the factor $0.9(d_h^2/d^2 - 1)^{0.5}$.

(b) The factor $_{A,Nb} = A_{c,Nb}/A_{c,Nb}^0$ takes account of the geometric effects of spacing, edge distance in the second direction and member thickness, where:

$A_{c,Nb}^0$ = area of concrete cone of a single anchor at the side of the concrete member, idealizing the concrete cone as a pyramid with a height equal to $c_1$ and a base length equal to $6c_1$ (see Fig. 63).

$$= 36c_1^2 \tag{41b}$$

$A_{c,Nb}$ = Actual area of concrete cone of the anchorage on the side of the concrete member, limited by overlapping concrete cones of adjacent anchors, by a corner or by the member depth; it may be deduced from the idealized failure cone (examples of its calculation are given in Fig. 64).

(c) The factor $\psi_{s,Nb}$ takes into account the influence of a corner on the distribution of stresses in the concrete:

$$\psi_{s,Nb} = 0.7 + 0.3\frac{c_2}{3c_1} \leq 1 \tag{41c}$$

For anchorages in a narrow member, the smaller value of $c_2$ of the two corners should be introduced in equation (41c).

(d) The factor $\psi_{ec,Nb}$ takes account of a group effect when different tension loads are acting on the individual anchors of a group:

$$\psi_{ec,Nb} = \frac{1}{1 + 2e_N/(6c_1)} \leq 1 \tag{41d}$$

with

$e_N$ = eccentricity of the resulting tension force of the tensioned anchors with respect to their centre of gravity

*Comment*
The eccentricity should be determined for the row of tensioned anchors closest to the edge.

(e) The factor $\psi_{ucr,Nb}$ takes account of the position of the fastening in cracked or non-cracked concrete:

*Fig. 63. Idealized concrete cone and area $A_{c,Nb}$ of cone at the side of the concrete member for a single anchor: (a) side view; (b) plan view*

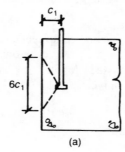
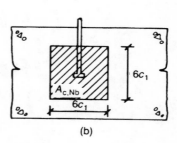

(a)  (b)

*Fig. 64. Examples of actual areas $A_{c,Nb}$ of the idealized concrete cones for different arrangements of anchors (loaded in tension) in the case of blow-out failure; (a) group of two anchors at the edge; (b) group of two anchors at a corner; (c) group of two anchors in a thin member*

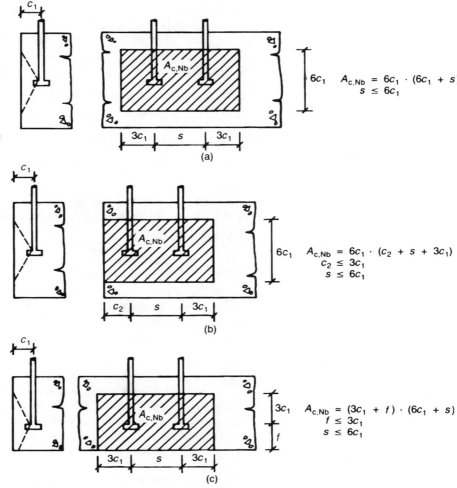

$$A_{c,Nb} = 6c_1 \cdot (6c_1 + s)$$
$$s \leq 6c_1$$

(a)

$$A_{c,Nb} = 6c_1 \cdot (c_2 + s + 3c_1)$$
$$c_2 \leq 3c_1$$
$$s \leq 6c_1$$

(b)

$$A_{c,Nb} = (3c_1 + f) \cdot (6c_1 + s)$$
$$f \leq 3c_1$$
$$s \leq 6c_1$$

(c)

$$\psi_{ucr,Nb} = 1.0 \quad \text{for fastenings in cracked concrete} \qquad (41e)$$
$$\psi_{ucr,Nb} = 1.4 \quad \text{for fastenings in non-cracked concrete} \qquad (41f)$$

*Comment*
$\psi_{ucr,Nb}$ is identical to $\psi_{ucr,N}$ (compare equations (22h) and (22i)).

For fastenings at a corner or in a narrow member with $c_2 < c_1$ the concrete in the area of the anchor head should be confined by a closely spaced reinforcement (stirrups or spiral) with a spacing $\leq 50$ mm. The confining reinforcement should be designed for the tension force $N_{sk}$ acting on the anchor at the corner.

*Comment*
Equation (41) has been checked only for single anchors at the edge. The diameter of the failure cone at the side of the concrete member was rather large ($\sim 6c_1$). It is believed that equation (41) is conservative for groups at the edge based on application of the principles of the CC-Method to this case. With fastenings at a corner, the resistance to blow-out might be reduced more than calculated by equation (41) because of the missing restraint of the concrete in the second direction. Therefore, the concrete at the edge should be confined by a closely spaced reinforcement to ensure a failure load according to equation (41).

### 15.1.3. Resistance to shear load

*Comment*
For anchorages with the fixture embedded in the concrete, spalling of the concrete in front of the fixture might occur before the anchors take up a

significant load. In general, this spalling does not negatively influence the steel or concrete resistance of the anchorage. However, unacceptable spalling might occur under service load. This spalling may be avoided by placing soft material around the fixture. This procedure is particularly recommended for fastenings close to edges.

*15.1.3.1. Required verifications.*　Section 9.3.1 applies.

*15.1.3.2. Steel failure: shear load without lever arm.*　Section 9.3.2.1 applies with the following modification.

For anchors welded to the fixture by the stud-welding process, the constant $k_2$ in equation (28) may be increased to $k_2 = 0.75$.

> *Comment*
> The constant $k_2 = 0.75$, compared with $k_2 = 0.6$ in equation (28), takes into account the influence of welding on the shear resistance.

*15.1.3.3. Shear failure: shear load with lever arm.*　Section 9.3.2.2 applies.

*15.1.3.4. Concrete pry-out failure.*　Section 9.3.3 applies with the following modification.

The value $N_{Rk,c}$ calculated according to section 15.1.2.4 should be inserted in equation (30).

*15.1.3.5. Concrete edge failure.*　Section 9.3.4 applies.

> *Comment*
> For anchorages close to an edge or corner and loaded in shear towards the edge, concrete failure may occur at rather small displacements. In general, for anchorages with a clearance hole in the fixture there is a gap between anchor and fixture. This gap may be larger than the shear displacement at failure. Therefore, only the most unfavourable anchor(s) should be assumed to take up shear loads when checking equation (1) of section 3.1 for the concrete edge failure mode.
>
> For anchors welded to or threaded into the fixture, the failure will start from the anchors closest to the edge. The peak load will be reached when the failure crack starts from the anchor furthest from the edge. However, the magnitude of the load increase may be very small for small anchor spacings. Furthermore, the fracture starting from the anchor closest to the edge may negatively influence the tension capacity of this anchor as well as the behaviour of the concrete member. Therefore, conservatively, the increase of the resistance caused by the anchor furthest from the edge should be neglected and only the anchors closest to the edge should be assumed to take up the shear load when checking equation (1) of section 3.1 for the concrete edge failure mode.

*15.1.4. Resistance to combined tension and shear load*
Section 9.4 applies.

**15.2. Fastenings with special reinforcement**

*15.2.1. Field of application*
Section 15.1.1 applies, with the following modifications.

For anchorages with special reinforcement to take up tension forces, the minimum anchorage depth is $h_{ef} = 150$ mm and the minimum edge distance in all directions $c = 1.5h_{ef}$. For anchorages with a special reinforcement to take up shear loads, the minimum anchorage depth is $h_{ef} = 100$ mm and the edge distance should not be smaller than the minimum values according to Table 7 (non-prestressed anchors) or section 15.1.2.5.1 (prestressed anchors). For anchorages with a special reinforcement to take up tension and shear loads, the minimum anchorage depth is $h_{ef} = 150$ mm and the minimum edge distance $c = 1.5h_{ef}$.

*Comment*
For fastenings close to an edge loaded in tension, a hanger reinforcement may be less effective than assumed in this Design Guide. Therefore, in case of tension loading and combined tension and shear loading the edge distance is limited to $c \geq 1.5h_{ef}$.

Special reinforcement may be provided to take up tension loads, shear loads or combined tension and shear loads. However, if special reinforcement is provided for one loading direction only, the resistance of the anchorage for the other loading direction should be calculated according to section 15.1.

### 15.2.2. Resistance to tension load

The special reinforcement (hanger reinforcement) to take up tension loads should comply with the following requirements (see also Fig. 65).

(a) In general, for all anchors of a group the same hanger reinforcement should be provided. It should consist of ribbed reinforcing bars ($f_{yk} \leq 500$ MPa) with a diameter not larger than 16 mm and should be detailed in the form of stirrups or loops with a bending diameter according to Ref. 1.

(b) The hanger reinforcement should be placed as closely as possible to the headed anchors and preferably tied to the anchors. Only those bars should be assumed to be hanger reinforcement, which are at least anchored with the bends in the concrete failure cone at an assumed inclination of 45°. Preferably, the hanger reinforcement should enclose the surface reinforcement.

(c) The hanger reinforcement should be anchored outside the assumed failure cone with an anchorage length $l_{b,net}$ according to Ref. 1.

(d) A surface reinforcement should be present which limits the width of cracks to a normal value ($w_k \sim 0.3$ mm), taking into account the splitting forces according to section 7.3.

*Fig. 65. Example for a quadruple fastening with hanger reinforcement to take up tension loads: anchorage depth $h_{ef} \geq 150$ mm, edge distance in all directions $c \geq 1.5h_{ef}$*

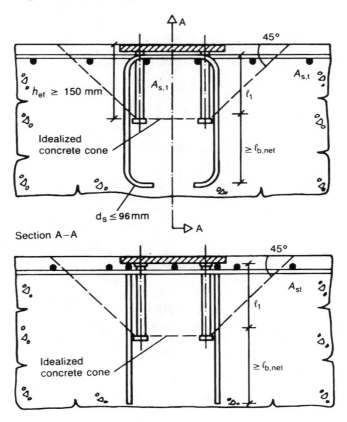

Section A–A

*Comment*
The inclination of the failure surface of the concrete cone is assumed to be 45° to account for possible variations of this angle. This assumption is conservative for the anchorage of the hanger reinforcement in the cone.

In practice, hanger reinforcement as shown in Fig. 63 is often provided to augment the tension capacity of headed anchors. In as much as this construction involves a circuitous load path to achieve the required embedment, it is recommended that the use of longer-headed anchors instead should be considered.

*15.2.2.1. Required verifications.* The required verifications are summarized in Table 8. For anchor groups, the same hanger reinforcement should be provided to all anchors.

*Table 8. Required verifications for tension loading — fastenings with special reinforcement*

|  | Single anchor | Anchor group |
|---|---|---|
| Steel failure of anchor | $N_{Sd} \leq N_{Rd,s} = N_{Rk,s}/\gamma_{Ms}$ | $N_{Sd}^h \leq N_{Rd,s} = N_{Rk,s}/\gamma_{Ms}$ |
| Pull-out failure of anchor | $N_{Sd} \leq N_{Rd,p} = N_{Rk,p}/\gamma_{Mp}$ | $N_{Sd}^h \leq N_{Rd,p} = N_{Rk,p}/\gamma_{Mp}$ |
| Splitting failure | $N_{Sd} \leq N_{Rd,sp} = N_{Rk,sp}/\gamma_{Msp}$ | $N_{Sd}^g \leq N_{Rd,sp} = N_{Rk,sp}/\gamma_{Msp}$ |
| Steel failure of hanger reinforcement | $N_{Sd} \leq N_{Rd,sl} = N_{Rk,sl}/\gamma_{Msl}$ | $N_{Sd}^h \leq N_{Rd,sl} = N_{Rk,sl}/\gamma_{Msl}$ |
| Anchorage failure of hanger reinforcement | $N_{Sd} \leq N_{Rd,a}$ | $N_{Sd}^h \leq N_{Rd,a}$ |

The partial safety factors for $\gamma_{Ms}$, $\gamma_{Mp}$ and $\gamma_{Msp}$ are given in section 3.2.3. For the partial safety factor $\gamma_{Msl}$ the value $\gamma_{Msl} = 1.15$ should be taken.

If $N_{Rk,sl}/\gamma_{Msl}$ and/or $N_{Rd,a}$ are smaller than the value $N_{Rk,c}/\gamma_{Mc}$ with $N_{Rk,c}$ according to section 15.1.2.4 and $\gamma_{Mc}$ according to section 3.2.3.1, then the hanger reinforcement should not be assumed to be effective.

*15.2.2.2. Steel failure of anchor.* Section 9.2.2 applies.

*15.2.2.3. Pull-out failure of anchor.* Section 15.1.2.3 applies.

*15.2.2.4. Splitting failure.* Section 15.1.2.5 applies.

*15.2.2.5. Steel failure of hanger reinforcement.* The characteristic resistance of the hanger reinforcement $N_{Rk,sl}$ for one anchor in the case of steel failure is

$$N_{Rk,sl} = n_1 \cdot A_s \cdot f_{yk} \tag{42}$$

with

$A_s$ = cross-section of one bar of the hanger reinforcement
$f_{yk}$ = nominal yield strength of the hanger reinforcement
$n_1$ = number of bars of the hanger reinforcement of one anchor

*15.2.2.6. Anchorage failure of the hanger reinforcement in the concrete cone.* The design resistance $N_{Rd,a}$ of the hanger reinforcement of one anchor in the case of an anchorage failure in the concrete cone is given by

$$N_{Rd,a} = \sum_{n_1} \ell_1 \cdot u \cdot 2 \cdot f_{bd} \tag{43}$$

with

$\ell_1$ = length of the hanger reinforcement in the assumed failure cone (see Fig. 65)

$u$ = circumference of the bar

$f_{bd}$ = $k_6 \cdot f_{bd}^0$

$f_{bd}^0$ = design bond strength according to Ref. 1 (see Table 9)

$k_6$ = factor that considers the position of the bar during concreting:

$\quad k_6$ = 1.0 for good bond conditions, as for (a) all bars with an inclination of 45°–90° to the horizontal during concreting and (b) all bars with an inclination less than 45° to the horizontal which are up to 250 mm from the bottom or at least 300 mm from the top of the concrete layer during concreting;

$\quad k_6$ = 0.7 for all other cases and for bars in structural parts built with a slip form

$n_i$ = number of bars of the hanger reinforcement of one anchor

*Table 9. Design bond stresses $f_{bd}^0$ according to Ref. 1 for good bond conditions*

| $f_{ck}$ [MPa] | 20 | 30 | 40 | 50 |
|---|---|---|---|---|
| $f_{bd}^0$ [MPa] | 2.25 | 3.0 | 3.6 | 4.2 |

*Comment*
The factor 2 in equation (43) takes account of the effects of the bending of the hanger reinforcement and of the confinement provided by the concrete on the bond resistance of the bar.

### 15.2.3. Resistance to shear loads

The special reinforcement (hanger reinforcement) to take up shear loads should comply with the following requirements (see also Figs 66 and 67)

(a) The hanger reinforcement should consist of ribbed reinforcing bars ($f_{yk} \leq 500$ MPa) with a diameter not larger than 16 mm. It should be detailed according to Figs 66 and 67. The bending diameter $d_b$ should comply with Ref. 1.

(b) The hanger reinforcement should enclose and contact the shaft of the anchor and should be positioned as closely as possible to the fixture (see Fig. 66).

(c) The hanger reinforcement should be anchored outside the assumed failure cone with an anchorage length $l_{b,net}$ according to Ref. 1.

*Fig. 66. Detailing of the hanger reinforcement in the form of loops: minimum anchorage depth $h_{ef} \geq 100$ mm and minimum edge distance $c \geq c_{min}$*

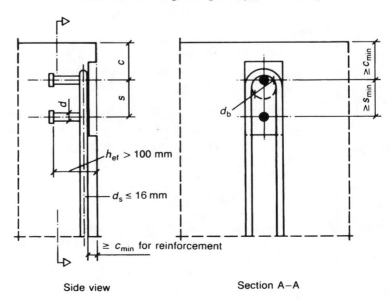

Side view          Section A–A

*Fig. 67. Hanger reinforcement: (a) U-loops; (b) V-loops*

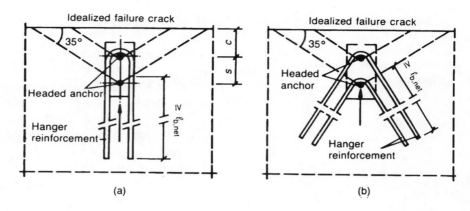

### 15.2.3.1. Required verifications.

*15.2.3.1. Required verifications.* The required verifications are summarized in Table 10. For anchor groups the same hanger reinforcement should be provided to all anchors.

*Table 10. Required verifications for shear loading — fastenings with special reinforcement*

| | Single anchor | Anchor group |
|---|---|---|
| Steel failure of anchor | $V_{Sd} \le V_{Rd,s} = V_{Rk,s}/\gamma_{Ms}$ | $V_{Sd}^h \le V_{Rd,s} = V_{Rk,s}/\gamma_{Ms}$ |
| Concrete pry-out failure | $V_{Sd} \le V_{Rd,cp} = V_{Rk,cp}/\gamma_{Mc}$ | $V_{Sd}^g \le V_{Rd,cp} = V_{Rk,cp}/\gamma_{Mc}$ |
| Steel failure of hanger reinforcement | $V_{Sd} \le V_{Rd,sl} = V_{Rk,sl}/\gamma_{Msl}$ | $V_{Sd}^h \le V_{Rd,sl} = V_{Rk,sl}/\gamma_{Msl}$ |

The partial safety factors $\gamma_{Ms}$ and $\gamma_{Mc}$ are given in section 3.2.3. For the partial safety factor $\gamma_{Msl}$ the value $\gamma_{Msl} = 1.15$ should be taken.

If $V_{Rk,sl}/\gamma_{Msl}$ is smaller than $V_{Rk,c}/\gamma_{Mc}$ with $V_{Rk,c}$ according to section 15.1.3.5 and $\gamma_{Mc}$ according to section 3.2.3.1, then the hanger reinforcement should not be assumed to be effective.

*15.2.3.2. Steel failure of anchor.* Section 15.1.3.2 applies.

*15.2.3.3. Concrete pry-out failure.* Section 9.3.3 applies with the following modifications.

The value $N_{Rk,c}$ calculated according to section 15.1.2.4 should be inserted in equation (30). Furthermore, the factor $k_3$ given in section 9.3.3, should be multiplied by 0.75.

> *Comment*
> In the case of fastenings with hanger reinforcement the anchors may be significantly deformed before failure. This will increase the force causing pry-out failure.

*15.2.3.4. Steel failure of hanger reinforcement.* The characteristic resistance of one anchor in the case of steel failure of the hanger reinforcement may be calculated according to equation (44):

$$V_{Rk,sl} = k_7 \cdot n_2 \cdot A_s \cdot f_{yk} \tag{44}$$

with

$k_7$ = efficiency factor = 0.5
$n_2$ = number of bars of the hanger reinforcement of one anchor

and with $A_s$, $f_{yk}$ as defined in section 15.2.2.5.

*Fig. 68. Anchorage at the
edge with a hanger
reinforcement to take up
shear loads under combined
tension and shear loads*

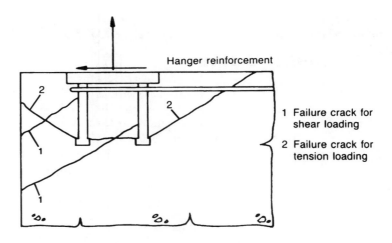

*Fig. 68. Anchorage at the
edge with a hanger
reinforcement to take up
shear loads under combined
tension and shear loads*

1 Failure crack for
shear loading

2 Failure crack for
tension loading

### Comment

The factor $k_7$ in equation (44) is smaller than 1.0, because it takes into account the influence of small deviations in the position of the hanger reinforcement (e.g. not in contact with the anchor shaft, or placed not as closely as possible to the fixture) and spalling of the concrete cover in the region of the loop. It is valid for anchors with a fixture embedded in the concrete and may be smaller for surface-mounted fixtures. If the correct position of the hanger is ensured (e.g. by welding to the anchor) then the efficiency factor may be increased; however, $k_7 < 1$ should be chosen.

For V-loops the angle of the bars with respect to the direction of the shear force should be taken into account when calculating $V_{Rk,s1}$. For U-loops it is assumed that the bars are placed parallel to the direction of the shear load.

### 15.2.4. Resistance to combined tension and shear loads

For anchorages with a hanger reinforcement for tension and shear loads, section 9.4 applies. For anchorages with a hanger reinforcement to take up tension or shear loads only, equation (33) should be used with $\alpha = 2/3$.

### Comment

For anchorages close to an edge with a hanger reinforcement to take up shear loads, failure cracks will occur in the concrete well before reaching the ultimate load (see cracks 1 in Fig. 68). These cracks will reduce the tension capacity of the anchorage. Also, the shear capacity of anchorages with a hanger reinforcement to take up tension loads might be reduced by the early formation of a concrete cone.

The behaviour of such anchorages under combined tension and shear loads has not been studied yet. However, it is believed that the given interaction equation is conservative.

# 16. Ultimate limit state of resistance — plastic design approach

A plastic design approach is allowed only for fastenings without hanger reinforcement to take up tension or shear loads which meet the conditions given in section 4.2.2.1.

Section 10 applies. However, the modifications for the calculation of the characteristic resistance for the different load directions and failure modes given in section 15.1 should be taken into account when applying the provisions given in section 10.

*Comment*
A plastic design approach is not allowed for fastenings with hanger reinforcement, because no experimental experience is available for this case. Furthermore, for fastenings with a hanger reinforcement the anchor steel may not yield, so that not much redistribution of forces may occur.

# 17. Ultimate limit state of fatigue

Fatigue loading of the fastening is allowed when the anchor is welded to or threaded into the fixture.

The following verifications are required for a single anchor, or the most loaded anchor of a group, to avoid a fatigue failure of the anchor steel.

$$\Delta N_{Sk} \leq \Delta N_{sk,fat}/1.25 \tag{45a}$$

$$\Delta V_{Sk} \leq \Delta V_{sk,fat}/1.25 \tag{45b}$$

with

$\Delta N_{Sk}$ $\quad = \max N_{Sk} - \min N_{Sk}$ $\hfill(46)$

$\max N_{Sk} (\min N_{Sk}) =$ characteristic value of the maximum (minimum) tension load on an anchor or the most loaded anchor of a group calculated according to section 4.3

$\Delta V_{Sk}$ $\quad = \max V_{Sk} - V_{Sk}$ $\hfill(47)$

$\max V_{Sk} (\min V_{Sk}) =$ characteristic value of the maximum (minimum) shear load on an anchor or the most loaded anchor of a group calculated according to section 4.3

$\Delta N_{sk,fat}$ $\quad = \Delta\sigma_{sk,fat} \cdot A_s$ $\hfill(48)$

$\Delta\sigma_{sk,fat}$ $\quad =$ characteristic fatigue strength for tension loading

$A_s$ $\quad =$ minimum stressed cross-section of the anchor

$\Delta V_{sk,fat}$ $\quad = \Delta\tau_{sk,fat} \cdot A_s$ $\hfill(49)$

$\Delta\tau_{sk,fat}$ $\quad =$ characteristic fatigue strength for shear loading

*Comment*
For anchor groups $\Delta N_{Sk}(\Delta V_{Sk})$ in equation (45) should be replaced by $\Delta N_{Sk}^h(\Delta V_{Sk}^h)$.

Values for $\Delta\sigma_{sk,fat}$ and $\Delta\tau_{sk,fat}$ should be taken from the relevant approval certificate or evaluated from the results of appropriate tests in the prequalification procedure.

*Comment*
For anchors welded to the fixture by the stud-welding process, the following values may be taken:

$\Delta\sigma_{sk,fat} = 100$ MPa

$\Delta\tau_{sk,fat} = 35$ MPa

These values are valid for $2 \times 10^6$ load cycles. For a larger number of load cycles they will be smaller.

For fastenings which are loaded by $N > 2 \times 10^6$ load cycles with the upper load equal to the allowable load, special checks may be necessary to avoid a fatigue failure of the concrete.

If the anchor is threaded into the fixture, values for $\Delta\sigma_{sk,fat}$ and $\Delta\tau_{sk,fat}$ should be taken from the relevant code of practice for non-prestressed screws.

# 18. Serviceability limit state

Part II, section 11, applies with the following additions.

For fastenings with a hanger reinforcement to take up tension loads, the following check is always required:

$$N_{Sk} \leq N_{Rk,c}/1.3 \tag{50}$$

with

$N_{Sk}$ = characteristic tension load on a single anchor or group of tensioned anchors, respectively, calculated according to section 4.2.1, with $\gamma_G = \gamma_Q = \gamma_{ind} = 1.0$

$N_{Rk,c}$ = characteristic resistance in the case of concrete cone failure of a single anchor or a group of tensioned anchors, respectively, calculated according to section 15.1.2.4

*Comment*

For tension loading, a hanger reinforcement will be effective only after the formation of a concrete cone. Because this cone should not be formed under service load, the check according to equation (50) is required.

For shear loading, a hanger reinforcement in contact with the anchor shaft will take up load when the anchor is displaced, thus delaying the formation of a concrete cone well beyond the admissible service load.

If the characteristic displacements under tension and shear load have not been evaluated by prequalification tests, then the following information should be considered as a first approximation.

The short-time displacements under the design tension load may be calculated from equation (51):

$$\delta_{No} = \frac{\epsilon_s}{E_s} \cdot (h_{ef} - t_h) + \delta_{head} \tag{51}$$

with

$\epsilon_s$ = steel strain of anchor
$E_s$ = modulus of elasticity of steel
   = $2.1 \times 10^5 \, [\text{N/mm}^2]$
$\delta_{head}$ = slip of anchor head
   = $(k_8/k_9) \cdot (p/f_{ck})^2$ [mm]
$k_8$ = 15 for $d = 10$ mm
   = 25 for $d = 15$ mm
$k_9$ = 200 for cracked concrete
   = 400 for non-cracked concrete
$p$ = concrete pressure under the head
   = $N/A_h$
$N$ = tension load on anchor
$A_h$ = bearing area of the head, as defined in equation (40c)

Under long-time loading the displacements will increase. To limit the displacements to an acceptable value ($\delta_{n,\infty} \lesssim 2$ mm), the pressure $p$ under the head should be smaller than the values of $p_{adm}$ specified below.

$$p = N_{sk}/A_h \leq p_{adm} \tag{52}$$

with

$N_{sk}$  = characteristic tension load on anchor calculated according to section 4.2.1, with $\gamma_G = \gamma_Q = \gamma_{ind} = 1.0$

$A_h$   = bearing area of the head, as defined in equation (40c)

$p_{adm}$ = admissible concrete pressure under the anchor head

      = $2.5f_{ck}$ for cracked concrete                   (52a)

      = $4.0f_{ck}$ for non-cracked concrete          (52b)

*Comment*

For an anchor group, $N_{sk}$ in equation (52) should be replaced by $N_{sk}^h$.

A significant increase of displacements will occur when the anchor is located in a crack and the crack width varies due to a variation in the live load. Furthermore, the displacements will increase under a sustained load due to the high pressure under the head. To limit this increase of displacements, the pressure under the head should be limited. The value given in equation (52a) has been evaluated from a limited number of tests for the criteria given in Refs 9 and 10. The value given in equation (52b) is based on current experience.

The short-time displacements under the design shear load may be calculated from equation (53):

$$\delta_{Vo} = k_{10} \cdot V_{sk}/d^2 \, [\text{mm}] \tag{53}$$

with

$k_{10}$  = $12 \, [\text{mm}^3/\text{kN}]$

$V_{sk}$  = characteristic shear load on anchor [kN] calculated according to section 4.2.1, with $\gamma_G = \gamma_Q = \gamma_{ind} = 1.0$

$d$   = anchor diameter [mm]

The long-time displacement under shear load may be assumed to be $\delta_{v_\infty} \sim 1.5\delta_{Vo}$.

*Comment*

For an anchor group, $V_{sk}$ in equation (53) should be replaced by $V_{sk}^h$.

# 19. Durability

Part II, section 13, applies.

# References

**Part I General provisions**

1. Comité Euro-International du Béton. *CEB–FIP Model Code 1990.* Thomas Telford, London, 1993.
2. ACI 355.1R-91. *State of the art report on anchorage to concrete.* American Concrete Institute, Detroit, 1991.
3. Comité Euro-International du Béton. *Fastenings to concrete and masonry structures, state of the art report.* Thomas Telford, London, 1994.
4. ENV 1991-1 (Eurocode 1). *Basis of design and actions on structures – Part 1: Basis of design.* CEN (Comité Europien de la Normalisation), Brussels, 1994.
5. Comité Euro-International du Béton. *International system of unified Codes of Practice for structures. Volume 1: Common unified rules for different types of construction and material,* CEB, Paris, 1978, Bulletin d'Information 125.
6. American Society of Civil Engineers. *Minimum design loads for buildings and other structures.* ASCE, New York, 1994, ASCE 7-93.
7. Thoft-Christensen P. and Baker M. *Structural reliability theory and its application.* Springer Verlag, Berlin, 1995.
8. Comité Euro-International du Béton. *General principles on reliability for structures — a commentary on ISO 2394.* CEB, Lausanne, July 1988, Bulletin d'Information 191.
9. European Union of Agrément. *UEAtc technical guide for anchors for use in cracked and non-cracked concrete.* UEA, London, 1992, M.O.A.T. 49.
10. European Organisation for Technical Approvals. *Guideline for European technical approval of anchors (metal anchors) for use in concrete.* EOTA, Brussels, Sept. 1994.

    Part 1     Anchors in general
    Part 2     Torque controlled expansion anchors
    Part 3     Undercut anchors
    Part 4     Deformation controlled expansion anchors (in preparation)
    Part 5     Bonded anchors (in preparation)
    Annex A    Details of tests
    Annex B    Tests for admissible service conditions, detailed information
    Annex C    Design methods for anchorages
11. American Society for Testing Materials. *Standard specification for performance of anchors for use in cracked and non-cracked concrete.* ASTM, Philadelphia (in preparation).
12. Deutscher Ausschuß für Stahlbeton. *Hilfsmittel zur Berechnung der Schnittgrößen und Formänderungen von Betontragwerken (Aids for the calculation of action effects and deflections in concrete structures),* Heft 240. Ernst & Sohn, Berlin, 1976.
13. ISO 3506: 1979. *Corrosion-resistant stainless steel fasteners; specifications.*